D1414635

MEASUREMENT
OF CONSUMER INTEREST

CONFERENCE ON EXPERIMENTAL METHOD

Sponsored by the

UNIVERSITY OF PENNSYLVANIA

May 1946

PARTICIPANTS

Paul H. Musser
Alfred Politz
Archibald M. Crossley
Malcolm G. Preston
A. B. Blankenship
J. R. Doubman
J. Stevens Stock
Estelle Ellis
J. Parker Bursk
L. L. Thurstone
Francis W. Irwin
Louis Guttman
Colston E. Warne
John S. Adams, Jr.
Edgar A. Singer, Jr.
W. Edwards Deming
C. West Churchman
A. G. Ashcroft
S. S. Wilks
Paul Peach
Ralph F. Breyer
J. H. Curtiss
D. H. Palmer
Morris Hansen
Samuel G. Barton
A. N. Watson
Russell L. Ackoff
Morris S. Viteles
Dorwin Cartwright

MEASUREMENT
OF CONSUMER INTEREST

Edited by

C. WEST CHURCHMAN

RUSSELL L. ACKOFF

MURRAY WAX

Philadelphia

UNIVERSITY OF PENNSYLVANIA PRESS

LONDON: GEOFFREY CUMBERLEGE

OXFORD UNIVERSITY PRESS

1947

CONTENTS

INTRODUCTION

By
C. West Churchman
Russell L. Ackoff
Murray Wax
Department of Philosophy, University of Pennsylvania

THAT modern science is facing a crisis in methodology, no serious student can deny. We are passing beyond the age of the nineteenth-century giants, whose contributions in the main were ascribable to the individual genius. Most of the problems of present experimental science cannot be handled adequately by one man, or within one field.

To consider but a few examples. There was a time when the experimental physicist could ignore the contribution of the psychological characteristics of the observer to his final results. He felt that he could set up experimental operations which could be performed in much the same manner by all normal individuals. But the advances in experimental psychology have shown us that the behavior patterns of individuals, even in relatively simple stimulus-situations, differ radically: the thresholds of sensation, the sensitivity, the intelligence characteristics, are all psychological measures that vary among the normal individuals of a culture. Hence the future of precision in all experimental fields will have to depend more and more upon the advances in experimental psychology. Even attempts to reduce the effect of the observer will have to depend upon a study of those aspects of observation which remain more or less invariant. We are just beginning to become aware of the importance of sociological measures in this connection; the way in which we represent the results of an experiment, the meaning of these results, and their most fruitful interpretation are evidently matters whose adequate handling depends upon a future experimental science of society.

Again, the industrial engineer could at one time consider the problem of the most efficient design of a production process without recourse to allied fields; but the modern designer must enlist the aid of the physicist (in the design of machines), of the biologist (in the elimination of health-hazards), the psychologist (in the design of the most efficient working conditions), to mention but a few.

Perhaps the most important step in the realization that scientific activity must turn coöperative is the recognition of the special field of research called methodology. A physicist of but a few years ago could represent his results by a weighted mean and "probable error," and claim a confirmation of his theory if his results agreed "reasonably well" with the predicted values. But modern mathematical statistics has shown that there exist precise methods for evaluating data, and that the criteria of confirmation can be, and ought to be made, as precise as the criteria for an adequately designed apparatus.

More generally, the self-conscious philosopher has come to realize that philosophy should immediately undertake an important role in science. It should act as a coördinator of research in the sense that it supplies general criteria for the adequacy of an experimental investigation. The new role of philosophy is that of a critique of experimental techniques; it attempts to define the most general conditions under which a procedure is said to be experimental, a process is said to be in experimental control, a question is said to have meaning.

This role of philosophy may seem to be a glorified one, as though philosophical thinking were in some sense basic to all inquiry. The new philosophy, however, is insistent on the point that its own progress demands the same kind of coöperative effort as does progress in any field. The methodologist cannot devise his criteria of adequacy within the ivory towers of an endowed institution. He must come to know what scientists are actually doing, what they can do, what society demands they do, in order to formulate the idealized criteria of what scientists ought to do. These criteria differ from the actual behavior patterns of scientists or from the actual demands of a society, but they depend upon this sort of information. The philosopher of science who is unaware of the problems and activities of present-day science is as unproductive as the statistician who analyzes data without being aware of their sources.

The Conference whose proceedings are contained herein was called together by philosophers with the aim of coördinating research on a problem vital to our national welfare: the measurement of consumer interest. It seems almost too obvious to note the wide diversity of research fields which must be brought to bear on this one problem. We must know what a measurement is, what "interest" and "consumer" signify. We must know how to sample a population to obtain reliable information. We must know how to analyze the data obtained. We must know what questions to ask and how to ask them. We must know how to use the results of inquiry in the most efficient possible manner. The measurement of consumer interest thus involves (at least) the coöperative aid of methodologist, statistician, sampling expert, psychologist, and marketing researcher.

While it may have been optimistic to use the term "measurement" in connection with the subject-matter of this Conference, such optimism is believed to be essential to scientific progress in this or any domain. Some of the Conference participants will be found to express doubt as to whether present-day marketing research constitutes a science, and this doubt is well founded. But none, we hope, would assert that the way is forever barred to our becoming scientific in this field. Indeed, the modesty expressed by the researcher here might well be extended to all branches of present-day science. The physicist or chemist or engineer who thinks that the problem of an adequate method has been solved in his field is no scientist, and merely lives in a world of his own fancy. Any self-conscious researcher familiar with the actual experimental techniques employed in these fields knows that there are many unexplained features of the methods, involving unconfirmed "hunches" and uncontrolled intuitions.

To make all fields of research more self-conscious, to accomplish a better understanding of method, to determine the most fruitful steps to be taken toward making research scientific, is the primary aim of this Conference, its predecessor,[1] and those to be held in the future. The aim is similar to that of "operational analysis" discussed by Professor Wilks in one of the Conference's informal panels, except that the emphasis here is on a coöperative effort toward a more adequate method in the various fields of research.

These Conferences are themselves an aspect of a still more general program, to establish Institutes of Experimental Method which will act within research groups as consultant bodies on method. The Institutes would operate in a manner similar to that of certain statistical groups already in existence,[2] except that the scope of the work of the Institute would be more general. One cannot set down adequate criteria for the design of experiments within statistical theory alone; the knowledge of an expert in general methodology is also required.

It would be wise to emphasize the primary purpose of this Conference by describing in some detail how such Institutes could be organized, and hence carry out in general the aims of such coöperative efforts as are contained in these Proceedings.

[1] The first Conference on Experimental Method was held at Bryn Mawr College in May 1945, and covered the fields of statistics, psychology, and physics.

[2] E.g., at North Carolina, Columbia, University of California at Berkeley.

The Institutes would be divided into sections, covering the general field of method within science: general methodology, mathematical statistics, sampling methods, and history of science. The sections would roughly have the following function:

1. *General methodology.* Its general research problems would include the criteria of adequacy of an experiment; the criteria of efficiency within experimental research; the meaning of the basic concepts of science; the role of formal theory; the criteria of application; etc. If, as Dr. Blankenship suggests in one of the informal panels, marketing research is not yet scientific, then we ought to begin to formulate some very definite criteria which will guide us in the direction of science; these criteria are not easy to formulate, and it is very doubtful whether most specialists have the time, knowledge, or inclination to formulate them correctly. The task would belong to the field of general methodology, just as the task of formulating the criteria of an adequate solution of a differential equation belongs to the field of mathematics.

In the case of special problems the section on general methodology would assist by attempting to evaluate an experimental design from the point of view of its adequacy with respect to the purposes of the inquiry. To illustrate: Suppose that the specialist proposes to "measure consumer interest" by making a population survey of preferences for a given item. Will his experimental plan provide adequate data for his purposes? The general methodologist would question such an experimental design on the basis that it equates "preference" and "interest," that it presupposes that verbal questioning at front doors provides pertinent information about the desires of those questioned, etc. These criticisms need not be fatal; they are merely raised for the sake of making the method complete. They force the specialist, either now or eventually, to investigate certain phases of his techniques. In other words, the task of the general methodologist is to open wide the aspects of a given experimental design, so that science may investigate all phases of its inquiry. Unless we can formulate the conditions under which such investigations are at least potentially possible, our activity is not scientific. If we cannot tell why a certain kind of response indicates preference, then we cannot be said to be measuring preferences. This does not mean that the specialist must answer all conceivable questions; but the method he uses should always leave open such answering for other investigators, or for himself. Now the task of revealing all the hidden presuppositions of an inquiry is no small one; it demands the generalizing type of mind, that is also familiar with the history of experimental method and its philosophical analysis. The point we are emphasizing is that the field of general methodology is as specialized a field of research as physics or chemistry or biology; that the specialist in other fields must begin to seek more and more for the assistance of the methodologist. Only when such coöperative research takes place can methodology itself hope to advance.

2. *Mathematical statistics.* Its general and special research problems have become well defined in the past decade. Modern statistical theory has brought up to date the classical theory of errors and probability, so that we can define with considerable accuracy the formal methods for making inferences from a set of observations when certain general presuppositions have been made concerning the distribution functions and the method of drawing the observations. In particular, statistical theory provides a method for determining the "risks of error" inherent in any specific method of handling a set of data. The importance of its application to all fields of research, including the one discussed in these Proceedings, is now well recognized. It is to be noted that the general methodologist is directly involved in the work of the statistician in the question of how statistical presuppositions (e.g., of randomness) can be experimentally investigated.

3. *Sampling techniques.* As the informal panel on this topic clearly shows, the adequacy of an experimental design depends upon an investigation of the techniques for sampling. Modern social theory now recognizes that the "Complete count" is in general an expensive and inadequate way of investigating social groups. Further, since a complete count is usually an idealized construct, it is extremely difficult in practice to estimate how closely the completeness has been approximated. But sampling techniques can be operationally defined, and the errors associated with them can be estimated. From the point of view of the general methodologist, the advantage of the work of this section on sampling is that it formulates the method of inquiry in such a way that the presuppositions can be stated explicitly, and hence can themselves be investigated.

4. *History of science.* The inclusion of this section in the Institute of Experimental Method may seem surprising, until it is realized that all investigation in science is but an outgrowth of investigations made in the past. Scientific inquiry does not start and end with individuals; the modern-day scientists are simply carrying on investigations into problems they have inherited from the past. But so much of modern science ignores the problem of properly evaluating what the past has had to offer. And it is difficult to see how the specialist who is involved in the complexities of his immediate problem can make adequate investigations into the origins of his work; just as, in the case of the other aspects of experimental method, he must rely upon the advice of experts in the

history of science to determine what aspects of the past are to be used most fruitfully in the present.

The Institutes would then be organized with individuals in each of the above sections. The exact number of members would depend upon the scope of research which the Institute would be designed to cover. In general, in each of the sections, there would be individuals familiar with special branches of science: mathematical and physical, biological, psychological, and sociological. But if the research organization is restricted to one or more branches, then the membership of the Institute would be similarly restricted.

The members of the Institute would act as coöperators in any given research project; that is, the experimental scientist would feel free to consult with any of the members, and to act coöperatively with them in carrying out any program. The members of the Institute would also conduct their own research into general aspects of their fields, since advance in theoretical problems is a necessary condition in applied problems. The members would also conduct an educational program, the primary purpose of which would be *not* to teach the researcher all about methodology, statistics, etc., but to teach him how and when to use the aid of these fields. In other words, the purpose of such education should be to lay the foundations for the coöperation which is so essential to the future advance of science.

The Institute of Experimental Method has been sketched here in broad outline. It seems hardly necessary to point out that in its application to research groups it would have to vary in form and activity. But the moral of the outline and, we hope, the moral of the Conference, is that the future progress of scientific research, and indeed the future progress of all our cultural activities, depends upon such organized coöperation.

We wish to thank the members of the other sponsoring departments of the University of Pennsylvania—psychology, statistics, and marketing and foreign commerce—for their coöperation in planning and carrying through the details of the Conference. We should like to acknowledge our indebtedness to Professor T. A. Cowan of the School of Law of the University of Nebraska and Dr. W. Edwards Deming of the Bureau of the Budget, for their efforts toward the organization of the program. We also wish to make special mention of Dr. John S. Adams, Jr., of the philosophy department of the University of Pennsylvania, for his invaluable assistance and support. For their aid in the mechanics of the Conference we wish to thank Mrs. John S. Adams, Jr., Miss Judith Wingert, Robert Rueman, Sheldon Peterfreund, and the students of the University of Pennsylvania who so kindly volunteered their services.

Finally, we wish to acknowledge our indebtedness to Professor Emeritus E. A. Singer, Jr.; this Conference may be considered as a partial objectification of a program outlined in his lifework.

Permission has been granted by *Psychometrika* for the publication of Prof. L. L. Thurstone's paper, "The Prediction of Choice."

Permission has been granted by the magazines cited in Prof. Viteles' article, for the publication of the prints appearing there.

ADDRESS OF WELCOME

By
PAUL H. MUSSER
Provost, University of Pennsylvania

MR. CHAIRMAN, Ladies and Gentlemen: It gives me a great deal of pleasure on behalf of the general administration of the University to welcome you and to wish you well in your Conferences.

I feel at this moment as I did several years ago in this same room when I was asked to come over and greet a group of Summer School students who were studying music and being trained to be music directors in high school. When I entered, the instructor giving the course said to me, "Now, we are going to sing one more song and just after that you will get up and talk. You really need no introduction." The song they sang was a Negro spiritual entitled "Listen to the Bleat of the Lamb"—and I arose with those words echoing up and down this room, giving me a startling feeling of innocence. I think that as a Professor of American Literature what I have to say concerning your work here will not be sharply different in tone than that song inferred.

I might say this, however, in welcoming you, that we here at the University think it significant for a University to sponsor meetings such as this conference of the Institute of Experimental Method. The approach to a subject from the combined points of view represented by various divisions of the University is of no mean import. The problem of your concern, Consumer Interest, is among the significant ones of the post-war period.

The Conference also is interesting from another point of view. When professional scholars in philosophy bring into play in everyday matters their training in the philosophic point of view, pooling their efforts with those in sociology, psychology, and the other groups represented here in the room, the results of such combined study should be unusual. Perhaps this coördination and focusing of effort should go back in collegiate training to the undergraduate student. The graduate student then, and later when he becomes an expert, will naturally take part in the coördinating and focusing of his expert knowledge as a matter of course.

When I refer to undergraduate teaching I find in my own teaching in American Literature that the undergraduates tend to have their information pigeonholed. An undergraduate student will take a course in psychology, for instance, in the College, or one in sociology in the Wharton School, or a course in education, or in mathematics—but when it comes to using that knowledge, say in writing a review of a book, he does not bring all his knowledge into play. It is all pigeonholed in his mind, and he does not use in sociology what he may have learned in psychology, or bring into his course in Public Speaking what he may have learned in other fields.

We are trying to eliminate pigeonholing and are attempting to develop courses in which from the very nature of the materials in them the students will be obliged to use subject matter they have got from several other courses. For instance, there is a program we are developing in American Civilization, in which we do not merely take courses from American Literature or from history, sociology, or political science. We hope, on the contrary, to formulate courses that will interpret American Civilization in various of its phases, bringing into use in one course the expert knowledge of faculty members in various departments. Later the students will be carried over from the undergraduate level into the graduate field. There will result, we are convinced, a background for the student of a coördinated and varied approach to a subject, such as the work of this Conference represents.

At all events, I repeat that the officials of the University wish you well. We wish you satisfactory results in your considerations, and we certainly believe that this gathering is a significant inauguration of activities that may lead to most productive developments now as well as in the future.

PROBLEMS IN PRACTICE

PARTICIPANTS

CHAIRMAN: Alfred Politz, *Alfred Politz Research.* SPEAKERS: Archibald W. Crossley, *Crossley, Inc.;* Malcolm G. Preston, *Department of Psychology, University of Pennsylvania;* A. B. Blankenship, *National Analysts;* John R. Doubman, *Department of Marketing and Foreign Commerce, University of Pennsylvania;* J. Stevens Stock, *Office of Industrial Relations, U.S. Navy;* Estelle Ellis, *Promotion Director, "Seventeen."* DISCUSSION: Myron Heidingsfield, *Department of Marketing, Temple University;* Edward Benson, *American Institute of Public Opinion;* Wilbur Phillips, *Social Unit Institute, Inc.;* John D. Samter, *Edward Stern and Co., Inc.;* Carroll S. Moore, Jr., *Princeton, N.J.;* M. Starr Northrup, *Opinion Research Corp.;* F. K. Beutel, *School of Law, University of Nebraska;* W. Edwards Deming, *Bureau of the Budget*

POLITZ: The human mind is forced to start with some oversimplifications in classifying phenomena or activities. As an example of these oversimplifications, we find the present meeting concerned with a distinction between theory and practice. There is no doubt that any practical step, so long as it is purposive, is related or involved with theory, whether formally stated or not. On the other hand, every theory is instigated by practical experience and aimed at the prediction of future experience. So long as theory and practice are well understood as interdependent activities, progress is secured. Only if either of the two tries to take on a self-satisfying tendency does stagnation follow.

When Edison gave his first performance with his phonograph he was accused by some learned professors of cheating. At that time it was the representatives of theory who did not want to accept new facts demonstrated by practitioners.

We have similar situations in research. We cannot change the basic motivation of the human mind. Selfishness will always enter every profession, but knowing this phenomenon no one need let this fact discourage him. We have always one way to circumvent the difficulties if we are willing to give selfishness a new aim. If it is pride which expresses professional selfishness, let us try to be proud of recognizing weaknesses. Let us try to be proud of being the first ones who accept changes. Any weakness can be overcome only after it has been recognized as a weakness. The recognition of the problem is exactly as important as the solution of it.

It is in this spirit that the speakers at this conference came together today. They are willing to throw away their professional pride of achievement and replace it by being proud of recognizing weaknesses and failures, by being proud of worrying over lack of perfection. With this in mind, I would like to call on Mr. ARCHIBALD M. CROSSLEY, who will speak on . . .

EXAGGERATED RESPONSES IN POLLING

CROSSLEY: A couple of years ago, when Gallup and Roper and I were sitting on a committee in Washington, Gallup said to me, "I know you do not carry on polls except in election years; this is an election year; are you going to carry on a poll this year?"

I said, "Yes."

He said, "Are you going mad?"

I said, "I don't think I'll be alone in that case—we are all going to have our problems."

We all knew the election was going to be close and we know today that the election was close. It was not close in electoral votes; it was close in the popular vote, and very close in a number of states. As a matter of actual fact, if you want to be technical about it, you could have swung seven-tenths of one per cent and elected Dewey. By which I mean to imply that it was an extremely difficult election for poll-takers because so many important states were hard to predict.

Mr. Politz asked me if I would start off by presenting just a few of the problems that we ran into in poll-taking.

We who take polls never worry so much about the percentage of the population that is favorable to each candidate. We can come reasonably close to the percentages favorable to the candidates provided we know who is going to vote, what types, or how many people are going to vote, and so forth. This is exactly our problem. We know that nothing like the number of people will vote who swear up and down "Of course we are going to vote." One has to break them down and approach them with a negative angle before he gets anything like the true figure.

In Pennsylvania, as I remember, normally something like a third of the people that could vote just don't bother to vote. Yet they will tell you in polls, before the election, "Sure, I am going to vote; positively." We knew when we started out, in our own case—and I think some of the other poll-takers will check me on this—that there would be exaggeration in the number of people who would say they would vote, but we did not know on which side the exaggeration would be. Now if we could have said the exaggeration was more on the Roosevelt side, or more on the Dewey side, we would have had something to go by. As far as our organization is concerned, we spent most of the year of 1944, right up to October, trying to find the answer to who was going to vote, and we used a series of studies.

One thing we asked the people was why they were going to vote for Roosevelt or Dewey, and we tried to get the intensity of their response, that is, how sure they were that they were going to vote for a given candidate. We asked them whether they had made up their minds, and tried to set up a study on that, and we also asked a series of attitude questions. We even went into the negative and said, "It won't matter much to you if the other candidate is elected, will it? You aren't going to bother to vote, are you?" We even went that far, but we still got the exaggeration. Finally, before the election, we hit on a series of attitude studies which allowed us to decide very definitely that the inflation, or such inflation as existed, was actually on the Dewey side. That is, more of the people who said they would vote for Roosevelt actually did vote for Roosevelt than did those who said they would vote for Dewey. We think that out of this experience we have learned something important for all marketing opinion research, and that is, we need some means of getting the truth out of people, getting them to tell you the real fact. The people are not lying intentionally. That is not the point. The point is that a certain number of them feel that they have a definite desire and intention to do something, and then do not go out and do it.

In an election poll you have to figure out what they are going to do. The same sort of thing applies in a lot of the other work we do.

We do a great deal of work for magazines. We know, for example, that if you take a given magazine out on the street or ring some doorbells and show somebody a magazine that has not yet appeared outside of the office of the magazine, an advance copy, and ask them to go through it with you or ask them whether they have seen this magazine, they will go through it with you and say, "Yes, I have seen that." But they could not possibly have seen it. Part of the exaggeration is a desire to please—misdirected, of course, and part is due to real confusion. So in the magazine research we had to set up "confusion tests." On the radio we have employed push-button devices to test listener-appeal, and have rung up and asked, "What program are you listening to now?" We had pushbuttons to tell us when we hit the right program. Some would say they were listening to a certain program when their radio was not even on, or that they were listening to another program.

Now this matter of getting the real information out of people is the biggest problem that my organization has, and I think it is one of the biggest problems in all marketing research. Most certainly it is one of the most critical in the public-opinion poll.

Yesterday I looked at a report that showed a 99 per cent figure. I would rather not reveal just what the figure was in reference to, for the report happens to have been done by a competitor. I don't think anybody here would know about it, but nevertheless it was a 99 per cent favorable figure. I said to this organization—we are working for them too—"I think the figure is probably correct, but if I were you I should worry about getting people to believe it, because with a 99 per cent figure there is always a chance that something is wrong."

I think that in a great deal of our marketing research today we have somehow got inflation. Of course we try to get the inflation out of it; we should like all the help we can get to find out how to do it.

POLITZ: I would like now to turn to DR. MALCOLM G. PRESTON to give us his problem. . . .

PREFERENCE AND PERFORMANCE

PRESTON: Shortly before the war one of my colleagues was visited by an engineer who had invented a new signaling device suitable for use on automobiles. The novel feature of the device was its use of the principle of apparent motion which is frequently used on advertising signs. The device was fastened to the rear end of the automobile, and at the driver's will a streaming light could be caused to move to the left (thus indicating that he proposed to make a left turn, or to the right (thus indicating that he proposed to make a right turn); or it could be made to blink (thus indicating that he proposed to stop). The engineer recognized two problems which he needed to solve before he could interest a manufacturer in his invention. He needed first to be sure that his device was a better device, in one sense or another, than the conventional stop-signal. He needed, second, to know which of the many time relations governing the streaming of the light should be selected as optimal. For what interval of time should each of the lamps in his signal be lighted? What interval of time should elapse between those intervals during which each of the lamps was illuminated? The engineer who had invented the device was inclined to the opinion that both of the questions should depend for their answers upon an analysis of the preferences of a large and properly selected sample of people. He thought, in other words that the proper measure to use in evaluating his device in comparison with the conventional device was percentage of preferences favoring the one as against the other. He suggested also that a proper study of the preferences of such people for the various rates in which the motion could be animated would furnish an answer to the question: What are the optimal time relations to be incorporated into the device?

During the discussions among those who were concerned with the design of the experiment, which it was hoped would settle the two issues, another procedure was proposed, namely, the determination of the efficiency of the signaling device as a means of denoting the driver's intentions. This school of thought proposed that a synthetic device be constructed which would duplicate the situation of the driver behind the signaling device. By a proper study of his reaction time to signals from a conventional device and the experimental device, and by a proper study of the reaction times as a function of various rates in which the motion was animated, it was proposed to settle the two questions raised by the engineer. It is evident that the two experiments which were under discussion here differed not only in their technical aspects but also in respect to what they implied about criteria. The concept of the criterion is very often used in applied psychology. By a criterion is signified a measure of some characteristic which it is desired to predict either by means of a test or an experiment. While it is true that both of these experiments attempted to predict which was the better device, one of them yielded data which could be used to support a conclusion as to which device would be more marketable, while the other yielded data which might be useful in support of the conclusion as to which device would promote safer driving. We reflected on the fact that if the experimental device were clearly superior from the point of view of safe driving, and if the fact were known, then it might well be preferred and should be chosen in the market. These reflections raised the essential question with which I am now concerned, that is, to what extent preferences agree with demonstrated superiority as determined by synthetic or realistic experimentation.

The war interrupted the experimental program which was carried out in an effort to find answers to these questions, but at the same time it created many occasions in which the same problems were raised. For example, a variety of devices, varying in their demands upon the operator, were invented to increase the efficiency of our ground and airborne anti-aircraft weapons. It was characteristic of many of these devices that they could be mechanized in any of a variety of ways. Aircraft turrets, for example, could be made very responsive to the slightest motion of the controls, hence reducing the time necessary for the reduction of large errors of gun-pointing. On the other hand, they could be made relatively unresponsive to slight motions of the controls, thus reducing the variability in gun-pointing once the guns were on the target. Frequently decisions had to be made between two devices of different design, or between two devices of the same design but incorporating different construction constants. And in general two kinds of evidence would be sought, one consisting in statements of preference from engineers, designers, psychologists, and skilled operators, and the other consisting in the results of the assessment of the device in the hands of an operator who endeavored to use it, either under synthetic conditions or conditions closely approximating its use in combat.

I am now unable to state any generalization of results of this kind from a knowledge of all the work carried on during the war under military and naval auspices, since the organization of science during the war was not designed to keep everybody informed of what everybody else was doing in the way of war research, but I can say, from several years' intensive experience with a compact body of problems in machine and instrument design that the weight of all the evidence was in favor of the conclusion that stated preferences, even from experts—engineers and psychologists and military and naval officers acquainted with the principles of the mechanism—were a very poor substitute for the quantitative evaluation of the performance of the gadget in the hands of the operator. In illustration of this fact I might mention an experiment done in the early years of the war which was designed to test whether one of two types of aircraft turret control mechanisms which was markedly superior, as judged by errors of gun-pointing in early practice, would maintain its superiority as the operator became more and more skilled. Because of a shortage of operators, one of my colleagues in the direction of the research volunteered to undergo the experimental training with the two types of controls. He was thoroughly familiar with the controls, he knew which of the two was superior in early practice, and he knew what the object of the experiment was. Despite these facts, at the conclusion of the training period he had no insight into the difference of the performance of the two controls. It was very striking that when the performance curves were disclosed to him, showing a striking tendency for improvement to occur with one of the controls, and no improvement with the other, he contended that there must have been some error in the record keeping, since the results as summarized were just the opposite from what he believed they were from his protracted experience in the turrets.

Now I do not wish to minimize the difficulties which confront the engineer or the psychologist who is endeavoring to collect data on the performance of man and machine under conditions of normal use. Much remains to be done, for example, before the so-called synthetic experiment can be conducted in such a way as to yield data which may be used unreservedly. Neither do I wish to contend that under all circumstances there is little or no correlation between expressed preference and demonstrated performance. I wish rather to give emphasis to the position that preferences and measures of performance imply different criteria, and that it is always a question of fact whether, first, they correlate, and second, with what sign, i.e., positive or negative.

POLITZ: Dr. Preston, I was wondering whether it would be worth while just to mention that the kind of problem you have reviewed, which was taken from a specialized field, is applicable to every other field of research. We sometimes have to run surveys in which people will be asked, "Which of the two or three do you prefer?" when one of the items is not in existence. Somebody will say, "Do you like radio with or without advertising?" It is the lack of imagination at that very moment that suddenly distorts the answer and gives us something that we can't use because the people can't imagine that without advertising they might have to pay directly. I only go a little into these generalities or generalizations so that you will not think you are restricted to the particular field in which the problem came up.

I would like now to turn to DR. A. B. BLANKENSHIP and have him give us his worries, . . .

THE RESEARCH CLIENT AS A PROBLEM

BLANKENSHIP: It seems to me that success in the measurement of consumer preferences depends upon technical "know-how" and a competent staff. It also rests upon the ability to sell the procedure and results to those who should display interest. This may be termed the problem of public relations.

Since I represent a research agency, our public is our clients. We must be able to convince our clients that we have the technical competence to perform the work, and we must present the final results in such a form that action will follow from our recommendations.

The people for whom we do research are business executives. As executives, they are forced to know a little about a great many different things; without this they cannot manage the affairs of an organization. This means that the commercial research firm is doing research for a layman—one who knows little about research procedures—and the trouble is that many executives think they know how to run a business research project.

A basic difficulty in dealing with clients is getting them to appreciate the difference between a problem and a technique. All too frequently the client comes to us and says, "I have a problem. Here are some questions I would like to have asked of a cross-section of people in certain markets. Can you do it for me?"

Now the questionnaire is one of the basic tools of the research process. It is precisely one of those steps of technique which should be the responsibility of the research agency. If a patient were going to a doctor, the patient wouldn't dream of saying, "Doctor, here's a stethoscope. I'd like you to listen to my heart."

Business generally has a problem. The business doctor can help cure the patient by going through a planned series of steps: learning what the symptoms are, planning a laboratory test, performing the laboratory test, analyzing the results of the test, and making recommendations based upon the test and his general background.

Good business research, like good medical practice, is expensive. In the field of medicine, a patient seldom "shops around" in order to get the cheapest price for medical service. Yet in business research that very thing frequently happens. The organization obtains estimates from many research firms, and buys the least expensive job. Research buying, like medical practice, should be based upon quality and confidence.

What are the steps through which the business doctor must go?

1. *He must first learn what the symptoms are.* In research terms, this refers to the nature of the problem. A patient does not go to a doctor with the statement that he has diagnosed his own case, finding that he has diabetes. Instead, the patient describes his symptoms. The doctor, from the symptoms and perhaps with the aid of laboratory tests, makes his own diagnosis and comes out with a recommended treatment.

Yet in the business field a client will often come to a research firm with a specific idea of finding out, for instance, if people like his company. Without knowing the background of the situation—the reasons the client thinks he needs that study—the research firm cannot, in the first place, decide whether the study is really required; and in the second place, the specific form it should take.

In order to develop a procedure which will help in his problem, the research agency needs to know that there will probably soon be a strike in the client's plant, and that he wants to know what he should tell the public in order to retain its confidence. This sort of statement tells the research firm that it must be sure to measure public attitudes toward the labor policies of the plant, as well as attitudes toward the plant union.

In other words, the general problem of the client in this case is to build a sound public relations program in the specific case of a strike. The research problem is to measure attitudes in such a way that this overall problem of the client can be solved.

2. *The doctor must next make plans for the laboratory test.* Just as the practising physician must frequently resort to laboratory tests in his diagnosis, so the business researcher must frequently depend upon a field study in order to obtain the facts of the case.

One of the first steps, as contrasted with the work of the physician, is the development and sharpening of the tool required for the analysis. The physician has standard procedures; in the business field a new questionnaire is designed for every study.

The number of tests to be made is usually specified by the physician. Oddly, in the field of business research, the patient often suggests to the doctor how many tests (interviews) should be obtained.

Even the nature of the tests—i.e., the nature of the cross-section— sometimes is defined by the business patient. Sometimes the suggestions are good, but it does seem a bit odd to have a doctor called in while the patient designs the tools for the analysis, plans the laboratory procedure, arrives at his own diagnosis, and finally prescribes his own medicine.

3. *Performing the laboratory test is the third step.* In the collection of business facts, one must be as careful and as thorough as the physician is in his planning of laboratory tests. Quality of fieldwork in business research is, in general, not given its proper emphasis. Yet poor quality in this phase of the operation can cause the results to be meaningless and even dangerous, since they may lead to the wrong diagnosis and recommendations.

Because this phase of the procedure is so important, it is essential to select the workers carefully, train them well, and supervise them at every point in the process.

Peculiarly enough, the average business patient pays less attention to this step than to any other part of the process. From the technicians' point of view, the entire field would be better off if clients of research firms forced them to pay more attention to obtaining quality fieldwork.

4. *Analyzing the results.* With sound training, the physician is able to consider all of the results, make his diagnosis, and come out with a recommendation. In business research we must be able to come out with generalizations based upon the results of the fieldwork, and end up with recommendations. Our recommendations, like those of the physician,

must consider not only the results of the laboratory test but also all other known pertinent facts about the patient's condition.

Oddly enough, the business patient sometimes thinks that he alone can interpret the meaning of research for his business. Imagine a patient telling a doctor to give him the diagnosis, and that he—the patient—will write his own prescription.

This point of view overlooks several facts. To begin with, commercial research interpretation is not easy—it is a job for technicians. In the second place, the actual process of translating the results into recommendations depends upon both technical knowledge of research and upon having a broad background of business experience. That is why the usual research firm employs persons who represent as many different fields of business as possible.

When the business doctor gives his prescription to the patient, there is one big difference between him and the physician. The business doctor must give the medicine in palatable form—otherwise the patient won't even take the trouble to bother with the treatment. The recommendations, then, must be given in simple, easy-to-get form. The style of writing must be clear; the form of report must be easy to read; plenty of illustrative material should be included. Without these the report will not be read by the busy executive, and might just as well have never been written. From my point of view, obtaining action based upon the report is a definite part of the responsibility of the research organization.

In conclusion, the problems facing the research firm in its dealings with clients are:

1. The client frequently buys research on the basis of the cheapest bid.

2. The client frequently confuses problems and techniques, and clients attempt to develop tools.

3. The client's description of the problem is frequently inadequate.

4. The client sometimes attempts to dictate the nature of the field job.

5. The client sometimes believes that the research organization cannot possibly interpret the results of the laboratory test as well as he himself can.

6. The client sometimes fails to act upon the recommendations based on research.

What should those in the business research field do?

It is clearly our responsibility to educate our clients.

POLITZ: I would like to turn to MR. J. R. DOUBMAN and hear what he has to say on . . .

AN EXPERIENCE IN CONSUMER EDUCATION

DOUBMAN: During the war I was asked if I would take the chairmanship of the Defense Council group on Organization of Consumer Interests, a very fine committee. It was a large committee, but it was composed of a true cross-section of consumers and various other interests. There was no group of consumers, from the smallest to the largest, that was not represented, with varying shades of ideals or ideologies from red to pink to pure white.

After we had met a few times we decided that there was one thing that was decidedly needed by the consumers of Philadelphia, and that was some place at which they could be trained in the weighing of values of various or varying items. We conceived the idea of a course which could be given to these people, and a considerable portion of my efforts was aimed at producing such a course and at getting a method of presenting it to the people of Philadelphia.

We worked up the course—it was long and comprehensive. There were contributions by practically all of the authorities in the varying fields we could think of. We started with the assumption that this great consumer organization needed direction through training—a Consumer Group. Therefore, we got together with the Philadelphia Public School System, and they decided that they would put this course in as part of their evening school program. They set aside appropriations to pay the teachers. It was our job, therefore, first to train the teachers. We began with a group of about two hundred teachers, and we got authorities in every field to come and talk to them so that they would be conversant with consumer problems. They went through a course in August and September and were ready to teach in October, when evening school started.

The Public School System provided the teachers; we supplied their training; and there were thirty-five school buildings in the city at which this training could be given. In addition to that, our committee attended to the publicity. I think we had as fine a publicity program as existed for any type of activity during the war period.

First, I remember that the Council of Defense had posters put out. They were posted on the front of the trolley cars and in all the subway stations. It was called PHILADELPHIA'S THIRD FRONT, to help in the drive against inflation by wise buying, and to have the consumers stretch their money further.

As a matter of fact, the Philadelphia School System likewise had pamphlets made up which were given to every schoolchild in the City of Philadelphia. I recall that I alone addressed probably some twenty organizations from settlement houses to women's clubs and churches and men's service clubs, bringing out the necessity for this educational advantage. There was a luncheon tendered to me at the Warwick, and I remember that practically every radio commentator attended it, and they were all extremely enthusiastic about the program when they saw it, and about the possibilities of extending this type of work. Every morning on the radio there was an advertising plug for Philadelphia's Third Front; there was a division coöperating with retail stores and practically every retail outfit doing any advertising, putting the slogan and the idea and the information before the public in their retail advertising. As a matter of fact, I recall that President Roosevelt went on the air talking about the question of inflation, and he talked one minute over the half-hour time, and we were given twenty-nine minutes directly following him on one of our Philadelphia stations, to present our point of view. During that month I think you would find that we probably had more space devoted to the problem of consumer training and education than had previously been devoted or was devoted during that particular time to the sale of bonds.

The thing was all set. It was just one of those things that seemed to be so "natural" that everybody was extremely interested in it. The night came for registration, and when it opened we were up against a rather unusual situation, because we had all of the thirty-five school buildings ready to receive our prospective students, and after all that expenditure, which would have reached hundreds of thousands of dollars, had we paid for that space, we had the interesting experience of having just two people register for the course.

Now, "Mr. Anthony," the problem I present to you and to the rest of the folks is this: Just how strong is this consumer movement—I know you are all interested in this consumer interest movement—but just how strong is it, and how are we going to hit the consumers? We could not do it in the City of Philadelphia.

By the way, after a three-weeks' registration period, we had one class of thirty people, and all the preliminary work of training and advertising and publicizing was devoted to the matter of training those thirty, and since that time there has been no widespread demand for that type of course.

My only question (and I am not questioning the value of the consumer movement—I think originally it was probably inspired by agitators rather than true consumers) is how are we going to measure this interest in consumer interest? I don't believe our experience was typical; I can think of several reasons why the difficulty existed at that time. Probably people were making too much money to worry about the question of how they should stretch their dollars. I don't know what the answer is, but I know what the results were, so that from my standpoint I am simply contributing an experience in this city which was extremely discouraging to our committee, and although we went on, I think that possibly some of the life was taken out of the consumer movement. We could have aroused consumer interest had we analyzed specific products, such as does *One Hundred Million Guinea Pigs*. Interest could have been aroused if we had taken this or that product, picked it apart, analyzed it, criticized it, evaluated it, and so on. People are always interested in that type of sensationalism, but for general principles to be established in the field of purchasing and to get the most out of their money, how are we to arouse the consumers and how are we to get their reactions to things? I am sitting here between two research folks, on my right and left. They know the jobs they do. As a matter of fact I am interested in their techniques and results, but as a practical matter I am disturbed by this experience. So if you have an answer to it, maybe the time is ripe to make another experiment. But I assure you, the next time I should have to see a great deal more interest on the part of the concerted consumer movement than I have experienced up to the moment. This remark is not meant too critically, but merely in the hope that we shall be able to find some way out of this dilemma which we in particular faced.

POLITZ: I will now turn to MR. J. STEVENS STOCK who will discuss . . . .

THE PROBLEM OF CALL-BACKS

STOCK: The problem I wanted to discuss is one about which there is considerable argument and perhaps more heat than light. It is one that I do not know the answer to, because if I did it would not be a problem. That is, the discussion that has been going on for a number of years between quota and area sampling.

I am not, in ten minutes, going to attempt to review the whole problem, but I should like to discuss some of the things we found out about the problem of call-backs in area sampling.

One of the main problems of area sampling is the cost. I believe that if we could diminish the cost per interview, area sampling would be more marketable, and there would not be so much disagreement as to quota sampling versus area sampling.

One of the characteristics of area sampling is that you predetermine the person you are going to interview. You know before you start whom you have got to see, and the experience is, in our modern cities especially, that the fellow isn't home. Now area sampling depends on the notion that everybody has a home, and if you sample homes you will have sampled everybody. If you set out a series of people to be interviewed, selected by area sampling, and say that you must see those people, you will find when you are through that the great majority of the people you set out to see you couldn't find, and the social characteristics of the people you have found would be different in many respects from those of the people you did not find.

We performed a number of experiments on this, considering just householders as the unit, and found, for example, by calling back time after time after time that the people we missed were the small family people. Also, the people we missed had a large number of workers in the family, and there was the tendency, therefore, toward a higher income.

We found a striking difference as to the characteristic of migration. For instance, in Washington, D.C., a number of years ago, we set out to interview so many dwelling units to find if that family had lived there a year ago last Christmas, or some such question. On first call we found two per cent said they had not lived there a year ago last Christmas. We were calling them migrants, but there was a large proportion, actually 30 per cent, who were not at home. There was no adult at home who could give us the answer to the question. We called back a second time. Of those we found on the second call we noted four per cent had not lived at that address a year ago last Christmas. On the third call we found that seven per cent had not lived at that address, and finally on the fourth call we found that sixteen per cent were migrants under that definition.

Now this problem of calling back is very expensive. Actually we used to figure that it would cost us a dollar per interview to get the interviewer from the home office out to the person to be interviewed. If the person was not at home, that was two dollars. Before you knew it, there was a tremendous cost involved when you started to make several calls, because we found, using the household as a unit, that in a large city like Philadelphia, in thirty per cent of the households no one was at home.

When we selected individuals, we found it even worse. Sixty per cent of the individuals to be called on were not at home. Now the question immediately comes to mind: If these social and personal characteristics are different, how badly would the results be biased if it were an attitude sample of some kind? We found some interesting things. The attitude sample we were conducting was toward certain aspects of the public's opinion of the war: some of the worker-motivations of defense workers and the like. We found the only difference between the people we got on the first call and the people we had to go back to several times was that there was a sharpness of the latter's opinion—their intensity was higher.

Now when Mr. Crossley was talking a moment ago, I wondered what part of that problem of inflation—and I am presenting a problem to him—what part of the problem of exaggeration is due to the fact that you are interviewing people on the street, people who were not at home, whose interviews are sharper. Perhaps some parts of his problem may possibly be eliminated by interviewing at home. We did find not more yeses or noes, but more intensity on the part of people we had to call back on several times.

There were certain compromises we attempted to use to solve the problem of not-at-homes. One was that the interviewers would be instructed to go around the block. We would try to assign more than one interviewer to the block. We instructed the interviewer to do his business elsewhere and go back and call again. We tried to make him call back once more and then accept a substitution. We tried to get the interviewers to interview as much as possible in the evening—which helped somewhat.

We found one solution which was pretty good, but perhaps costs more than the calling back. That was the principle of the double sampling, and it was useful when the final interview to be conducted was a long, expensive one.

We ran a preliminary survey to obtain a variety of factual data only on every member of approximately ten thousand arealy selected dwelling units in each large city. In doing this we accepted any adult member of the household who could give us the factual data on the remaining members. At times we would accept the word of a near neighbor on the family characteristics. This preliminary survey thus was not seriously hampered by not-at-homes, and since it obtained only a few factual data it was relatively inexpensive. Along with the factual characteristics gathered in this enumeration we would find out at what time of day or evening each adult in the selected households was most likely to be at home.

Since these ten thousand dwelling units contained from twenty to thirty thousand adults, we thus had built up a sizable panel which we could stratify by any of the enumerated characteristics and from which we could select a smaller sample for revisit and further interview. The persons thus selected were known not only as to certain social characteristics but as to what time the interviewer should call. This large panel could be used over and over again in the selection of smaller interview samples. In this way the cost of this preliminary enumeration was absorbed by many different surveys. Even so, we had great difficulty in reducing the cost of this preliminary survey sufficiently to make the method of double sampling practicable.

How many call-backs should be made in areal sampling for safe economical results on any particular survey? I have no answer.

POLITZ: I have no answer because it puts us all in the same boat. I think we can go a step further and agree with your opinion that it is a general problem that faces us, whether to use the area or the quota type of sample.

With this I should like now to turn to our last speaker at our table, Miss Estelle Ellis. She distinguishes herself from the rest of the speakers first by her sex and second by her profession. In contrast to the rest of us who work in research, she is one of those "lions," one of the "nasty ones" who pay for it in the end, but before they pay they want us to do something in the line of doing it better—and what we do is always wrong, I suppose. So I think MISS ESTELLE ELLIS may tell us in what way we are wrong. She will discuss . . . . .

THE RESEARCHER AS A PROBLEM

ELLIS: I neither speak your trade language nor do I know enough about your problems to discuss them intelligently. However, at least I can hope to enlighten you on what my problems as a promotion director and buyer of research are.

To begin with, I represent a teen-age magazine; a publication edited for girls ranging between thirteen and eighteen years of age. One of our major problems has been to discover whether our story regarding the buying ability of this age group holds true. When we first decided to publicize the magazine to the trade, we went to available government sources for statistics regarding the teen market.

For example, we went to the Department of Commerce to learn if any research had been done on this particular age group's buying habits. Unfortunately we found a minimum of usable information. The statistics that were available were, in the main, superficial. While they could be used as a basis for general promotion statements, I didn't feel they were close enough to the picture to warrant my using them. I felt strongly the need for scientific research that could serve as a backing for my promotion copy.

This, therefore, was one of my major problems. The lack of adequate research in the teen field is a great handicap. It leads me to suggest that researchers concentrate on this newly discovered market. This recommendation is made particularly to those students in the audience who are thinking in terms of specializing in one particular field after graduation.

Another basic problem of mine arises out of my complete ignorance of research techniques. When I am in the market for a new research job, I am confused by the variety of solutions offered me by the research companies I consult. There are frequently as many as four or five interpretations of my problem offered, depending on how many organizations I call in. Each one of these companies has what it feels is the best idea of how to tackle my job. I cannot quite comprehend this diversity of opinion in a field that should come close to the scientific. This confusion, in my mind, makes an intelligent decision tremendously difficult.

I started out by telling Dr. Politz I had no problems. He is therefore probably amused by all of this. But I decided, after thinking over the last several research jobs we had undertaken, that I had my share of problems. However, I do feel that I may be able to offer a solution to a few of them.

It certainly would help me and, I think, eventually you research people, if you as a group would get together and standardize what you believe to be good research. Now such standards may be impossible to achieve, but they are worth working for. It certainly would reduce the confusion in the consumer's mind if the research presentations made by various companies did not differ so radically in essentials. For example, while one company tells us that a one-thousand sample is sufficient to give us scientific results, another organization insists that a five-thousand is the minimum necessary. And talking about the sample problem—let's say that the research organization convinced us that a one-thousand sample is adequate. We then have to do a selling job on the advertising fraternity since our salesmen frequently tell us that space buyers are not always educated to accept a small but scientific sample. This puts us in the position of defending research or paying out a great deal of money to get a larger sample, just so that we can satisfy an uninformed median man. You, as we, eventually suffer for this since the buyer of research is forced to cut down on the number of research jobs he can afford to do.

If the truth about scientific sampling were publicized, everyone, including myself, the advertising man, and the mass public would know enough to accept research as recommended to us by organizations such as those you represent. For this reason I believe that you, as a group, need first to educate the mass population to research standards as well as to the importance and necessity of research. You can do that only by telling promotion people like myself what to expect of good research. If you do that, you will help us afford, and appreciate, more and more research. It will eliminate the need for sending out an education piece with each research analysis. It will also obviate the need for enlarging upon a scientific sample.

There is another very large question in my mind. While many reliable research sources insist that the direct-mail type of survey is less desirable than the personal-interview variety, very little has been done to clarify the differences between these research techniques. Frequently an organization like ourselves will undertake a mail questionnaire for what we feel are less important research jobs. However, if this kind of research technique is not acceptable or cannot give us scientific results, its use should not be tolerated at all. Here again, if research criteria were publicized there would be no question in the consumer's mind as to what kind of research he needed for a particular job.

POLITZ: Thank you very much, Miss Ellis. I would like to add only one word of advice to those who are buyers of research and therefore may be on the same side of the fence that Miss Ellis is at present, and may be bothered by some of her problems in talking to research men. I think at least one thing should be borne in mind, and perhaps it might be some kind of guidance for our further discussion: that is, let us throw away the pretense that research has anything to do with science.

It is our aim to be scientific. But there is a great danger whenever we find trades assuming to be scientific by using scientific terminology. I should say that if we want to make a distinction, we are willing to agree that engineering, chemistry, physics certainly are on the level of a science, and that economics, psychology, sociology are on the way of perhaps sooner or later becoming sciences. But the danger is that the terminology is way ahead of scientific achievements. It is not by any means true that the scientific capabilities of those working in economics or sociology or psychology are less developed than among those working in chemistry and physics, but the point is that in chemistry we have something bigger than the human mind to check our mistakes by. If a chemist for some reason puts together a compound that explodes in his laboratory, he will be moved out of his job of chemist, no matter how skillful his terminology is, but if the psychologist makes a mistake by improperly analyzing a subject, at least he won't blow himself up and he may become very famous. I don't mean to say the psychologist is on a lower level of scientific ability, but he has nothing to be checked against, and only if we have a check bigger than the human mind can we evaluate a selected sample.

Therefore I would say to Miss Ellis, don't be surprised if we have disagreement. I think that is the beauty of these meetings, that we have a means to help us to furnish evidence that we may become scientists sooner or later. But don't take it from a research man that he *is* a scientist, and if he says he is, he is dangerous.

DISCUSSION

HEIDINGSFIELD: I would like to ask of Commander Stock a question with reference to area sampling. You say the problem of call-back is a difficult and expensive one, but I don't think you brought out the problem of refusal that so often confronts us. When you do a survey and find that ten or fifteen or twenty per cent of your group have refused to answer, after the first question, or even after the introductory statement, it seems to me that would act as an indication of a population characteristic which may make a tremendous amount of error in the final analysis of our sampling job. I should like to know whether you have had experience on that particular problem, and if so, what have you done?

STOCK: We have always suspected in refusals, two things. One, the selection and training of our interviewers; two, the development of our questionnaires. The questionnaire perhaps may not be worded nicely. I don't know, I have had no experience where refusals have been as high as 20 per cent—they have only been two or three per cent at the worst, and therefore have been relatively a minor problem as compared with the call-back. But we have suspected our recruitment, training of interviewers, and the questionnaire—not the social phenomenon.

HEIDINGSFIELD: I should like to ask one more question. Would it be thought by this group, with regard to the percentage of refusals on a survey, if after a re-sample you have found the same characteristic of a percentage of refusals, we might be able to consider that as a characteristic of the population.

POLITZ: If I understand you rightly, in reference to the refusal, at least to try to go back and take a sample of the refusals; is that what you have in mind?

HEIDINGSFIELD: Yes.

POLITZ: As far as I am concerned, if you want me to answer, refusals to a certain point are relative to the topic. It does not follow that some one who refuses to answer on Topic A will refuse on Topic B. If we get a definite refusal, it means it is worth while to go back and interview these people from a different angle and therefore try indirectly to get further information about their characteristics.

BENSON: Commander Stock: you mentioned that the call-backs are a different type of individual from those who were at home on the first call. You also mentioned that they seemed to be more intense in their feeling. I think that is a very interesting point, and I should like to ask you two questions: If you could give us a little fuller definition of what you mean by more "intense" in their feeling, and how much difference did it make on the total result on the question when you added in the people you picked up on further call-backs?

STOCK: I was using the word "intense" where you have a multiple choice leading from one extreme to the other. Those found at the extremes were the call-backs. It was not the intensity that Guttman uses, where he follows with a question designed to measure intensity.

As to the second question, if we took an arbitrary central point, the percentage from the right to the left of that point did not vary significantly. The yeses and noes were no differently distributed among the call-backs than among the persons we saw first. Of course the problem was only one of an attitude toward work and motivation and the war. On consumer interest it may be another matter.

BENSON: If what you have stated held for all or for most problems, then would you say the expense of the call-back was justified, since the division of opinion is relatively the same?

STOCK: That I don't know. I know that where you want to learn something about whether a family is willing to buy washing machines and things like that, I should suspect there must be some value in calling back, because there is a considerable difference in family size, and the small, one-person families are not so likely to want to buy washing machines. But I believe that on the question of work motivation there was probably no reason to call back.

BENSON: Whether or not to call back varies, then, by the subject, you believe?

STOCK: Yes, and how to predict it before you start a particular study is hard to say.

PHILLIPS: I have perhaps a slight contribution to make to the field of discussion out of my actual experience.

About twenty-five years ago in New York, there was a debate whether milk should be raw or pasteurized and sanitized, and so forth. There were scientists who claimed that if milk was raw the consumer was exposed to pathogenic germs, and on the other hand there were scientists who adduced equally impressive evidence in support of the contention that if milk were pasteurized it destroyed the vitamins and caused rickets, constipation, etc.

As a result of the conference, the consumers did not know what to buy, the health departments did not know what to enforce, and the milk dealers did not know what to produce. To install a very expensive pasteurizing machine and then find the weight of scientific opinion was against pasteurization was a gamble; and, on the other hand, not to install such a machine and then to find that the weight of scientific opinion was in favor of pasteurization was an equal gamble.

I proposed at the time that we set up a commission of twenty-five of the greatest scientists in the field of human nutrition—sanitarians, chemists, bacteriologists, public health authorities, and so forth. We sent out an invitation and got our twenty-five men together—and they were the greatest men then in the field. The Chairman was Milton Rosenauer, who was then Professor of Public Health of the Harvard Medical School. We took this position: "You will hold as many meetings a year as you wish to, but when you come in you are all going to put your facts on the table and you are going to come out with unanimous decisions; we are not going to take anything less than unanimous decisions."

In other words, we said, "Here you are working off in this organization or in that laboratory. You don't know what we are doing in New York, and the other one over here doesn't know what the guinea pigs over here are doing. What you can agree on is a matter of further research, but for God's sake, coördinate your research."

Now believe it or not, within a year and a half that Commission, without any laws behind it whatever, had laid down a basis for the sanitary control of milk supplies; that is, the grading, the labeling for the consumers so that they would know what was good or bad milk. You know, up to that time you could put twenty bottles of milk on the table and nobody knew what was pure water, what was pure milk, or what was pure sewage! All you had to go by was the statements of the advertisers, and all the statements of the advertisers were exactly the same thing— they illustrated the bottle with a picture of cows beside a pearly stream, eating luscious grass beneath a blue sky with a few feathery clouds overhead. We all knew it was different. But believe it or not, as I say, within a year and a half we had standards which had swept the country.

The work of the Commission was later taken over by the Milk Division of the Public Health Service and those standards have been adopted in twenty-two hundred American cities and towns.

There is one point I should like to leave with you: that the development of criteria for judging any commodity should represent a consensus of national opinion, and it should represent the work of researchers whose work is coördinated. They should agree upon what they can agree upon, and should reserve for future coördinated research what they can't agree on.

The second point is on this question that the Commander was discussing. It so happened that during the First World War I organized an experiment. It was not an experiment in consumption; it was one in democracy and it was carried on in a unit of about 12,500 people. We took the blocks of about one hundred families as our basic unit, and we elected by proportional representation a council of representative men and women in each of those blocks, of which there were thirty. In other words, we had thirty blocks and thirty counselors and thirty working chairmen of those councils, who were not coming in from the outside to investigate on behalf of a teen-age magazine or a milk company or a research department, but actually represented the people. Now, curiously enough, we took the astounding position that the purpose of democracy and the purpose of industry was to meet human needs; and that our geographic organization should represent human needs.

Then, too, we were also pioneers in our position that while men are in the factory and the mines and the fields and the banks, it is the women who are in the home, and human needs are the needs of babies and children and members of the household. So all those block representatives were women, and within about six or seven weeks we had established through those women close, continual, friendly contact with every man, woman, and child in that whole area.

We had an Occupational Council that represented the skills. It was a two-winged organization. We found as we went along that we were collecting a lot of data—getting facts. We found these women were reservoirs of information. We found that in Columbus they wanted to study old people. There was no data about old people. Sixteen of the women volunteered, and came to our headquarters and pulled out the questionnaire, and without rising from their chairs every one of the sixteen women was able to supply the name of every man and woman over sixty years of age on the block, and answer every question on the questionnaire.

We finally said, "We ought to take a census in the district, but we ought not to take it without consulting the people." The national and city group brought us the questionnaire. It was discussed in that area by the occupational council and the Geographic Council for several weeks before they decided that the required information was valuable to the people. They held the position, "We can get no help or information from the people until we can show that there is a reason for getting the information."

Then we found that there were a number of different studies being made on health, tuberculosis, etc. We found that all the outside agencies, like your agencies, were sending in their strangers to knock on doors to get information—for what? Not for the people but for themselves, to be used for their own particular purposes.

We took one census and kept it correct. Our block workers knew when their people were at home. They knew their people. The census was corrected from week to week.

Unemployment is one of the major questions of the country. The United States Census Bureau takes an unemployment census every ten years. It sets up a staff all over the United States, and before it has even got together the facts, this or that community has been wiped out. But we kept our census corrected from week to week.

We found later that our technique could be used with regard to studying consumer needs. But the point I would like to lay before you is that those studies should not be made for any organization or by any outside agency. They should be made by the people themselves, because they are thoroughly convinced that the fruits of those studies will be of value to them.

BLANKENSHIP: May I comment on that? Rather than start a controversy, I will just take a couple of minutes to present my personal reaction to this suggestion. I think the speaker from the floor has overlooked a very, very important fact. It is true that the commercial research firms do tend to conduct research for a particular organization or perhaps a group of commercial organizations, but the only reason the commercial organization buys research or hires us for any other research, is to be sure that their business is going to be a sound one. After all, the consumer is naturally important to any commercial establishment, and must be satisfied. Therefore I think it quite in order to have commercial organizations, which are the backbone of the country, asking questions which may be confidential.

SAMTER: My question is on refusals. We came to the conclusion that refusals would be either due to a bad questionnaire or a poor interviewer or else be due to the actual refusal, a person who is a different type of person, and that therefore these refusers would affect the honest answer. Now, for example, you might have found out that the refuser had just as many ice boxes as the non-refuser, in a survey of those using different types of refrigeration. That would indicate that you should not go back to get refusals to answer. Now if you had got answers the second or the third time you went back, it would indicate to me that the reason for the original refusal was in the original question. If, on the other hand, you went back and got a small percentage, it would indicate to me that they were just the type of people that won't answer.

POLITZ: I would answer that there might be a small number of people who definitely refuse anything. There is one section of New York where as far as we can see no one can get an answer. I think the only way to get an answer would be to wave a ten-dollar bill through the window. I think we should not be too much afraid of changing the polls. On the other hand, once we change our polls we should not think that the new approach which gets the others in on the sample is necessarily the better approach.

SAMTER: But I am thinking of the people who are not interested in questionnaires. Those people may have an entirely different attitude from those who are interested in questionnaires.

POLITZ: I don't get the point clearly. I think the problem is how we approach them. What is the topic by which we open our discussion to them? I think it depends on the topic whether we get a refusal or not. One will refuse; another will not refuse on the same topic. Thus standardizing a questionnaire might put an obstacle in our way.

SAMTER: Have you had good results when you reapproach refusals with new questionnaires?

POLITZ: Oh yes.

QUESTION: There was an article in a recent issue of a national weekly about direct mail survey, in which an organization, after tabulating all their results, felt that, because of the number of refusals, they did not have a fair cross-section. They went back and made personal call-backs on the people to whom the direct mail questionnaires had been sent and who had not answered, just using those call-backs alone. In that way they made a separate survey to ascertain whether there was a difference in the answers. They found practically none, which might be one answer to how important refusals are.

POLITZ: I am inclined not to agree with the last point, because I think it does not solve any of our problems. If, for instance, we send out letters we expect answers, but we know of course that only a minority does answer. Now if we send interviewers after those who did not answer, and the answers check with those we got by mail, then I think we are entitled to draw the conclusion that the distortion which we have in our mail sample does not affect the results. But if any of them dares to go the next step and say, "Therefore mail service is always all right"; then he commits a critical fallacy.

MOORE: In the survey referred to, the conclusion was that among an homogeneous group that had the same community interest, these conclusions were valid. In that particular survey they used the magazine's subscribers, two-thirds of whom are college graduates. This was an important factor in that survey.

POLITZ: You used the word "homogeneous." For instance, since they are mainly college graduates, the assumption is made that they are therefore homogeneous in other respects, and there I think lies a point where doubt should enter, because being homogeneous in reference to being college students or some other things does not necessarily make them homogeneous on certain political matters. For example, they may disagree on racial questions or in their desire to buy a motor boat. It should be emphasized that the homogeneous group is only homogeneous on a certain matter.

DEMING: Mr. Phillips talked a moment ago on the desirability of research on unemployment. He may or may not be aware of the fact that there is a monthly report on the labor force. If he referred to one census of unemployment, I should like to know which one or when that was.

PHILLIPS: I am speaking of the last census of population. Of course there are estimates of unemployment, but I will guarantee that if you drew a circle within a radius of any home in Philadelphia embracing ten thousand people, nobody would know who was unemployed in that particular district.

DEMING: I should like to point out that there is considerable difference in the technique used in measuring unemployment in 1931 or 1937, and the techniques used at present.

PHILLIPS: The problem of measuring unemployment is something like the study of the national income which began under Dr. Mitchell in the national Bureau of Economical Research in 1918. There is always, however, a high factor of uncertainty in all those studies because they are made through complicated methods.

DEMING: The factors of uncertainty are known.

PHILLIPS: But the survey is nevertheless incomplete. When you contact every single home in the area, then your facts are incontrovertible.

DEMING: I don't believe there would be agreement on that point.

PHILLIPS: That is again a matter which I think has been demonstrated, and the cost is negligible.

STOCK: Could I ask Mr. Northrup, who worked longer than I with the monthly report of labor force, to describe how that is done and how the census is taken every few months?

NORTHRUP: Briefly, there is a national sample of some thirty thousand households interviewed each month for purposes of determining the labor force, employment, unemployment, characteristics of workers and characteristics of unemployed workers. That survey was initiated in late 1939 and was in operation at the time of the 1940 census, at which time the results checked very well with the national census results. It has been subject to technical committee review, and I agree with Mr. Phillips that there are still things we do not know about unemployment and employment. However, it does give a very good tool and we have found these results satisfactory in giving the current characteristics of population as well.

PHILLIPS: I appreciate the value of the work that is being done at the present moment in research. There is no other way of doing it, but after all, a sample of thirty thousand families in the United States is three for each unit of ten thousand people, and I believe it is much safer to take a survey of every family in the district than just three.

I should like to make one other point, too: The consumers spend tremendous money for advertising every year in the prices they pay for goods. I don't know how much it runs to now, but I know that Edward Bok in 1934 estimated it at a billion and a quarter dollars. That is $125,000 for every ten thousand population. That is all charged to the consumers in prices. In other words, the consumers pay for every bit of research done in this country, and there are innumerable agencies going into every locality from a multitude of organizations, each out after data for some particular use for itself. Very few, however, take the working hypothesis that this information is being secured for consumers as a whole, for everybody.

POLITZ: You are obviously concerned with the amount of money the consumers are spending, but it should put you at ease to realize that instead of conducting a complete census, the census is willing to get away with a sample of thirty thousand and thereby unburden our consumers of so much in taxes.

BEUTEL: As an outsider, I am interested in the point of law. I am interested in Dr. Blankenship's statements where he drew the analogy between the doctor and the scientific analyst, and in your statement, Dr. Politz, that there wasn't any such thing as science in research. I should like to hear what techniques you have for checking your results; what scientific techniques we have in this field. Is it really a science or simply a measure of guess work? You speak of this or that being checked. How do you check?

DEMING: There are two kinds of surveys, the one is the type you might call qualitative. In such surveys the answer to your question is a matter of judgment.

But there is another type of survey called quantitative in which the answer to your question is unequivocal. The margin of error is known in advance. When it comes to checks between a sample and a complete count or data from some other source, the statistician who designs a sample in the quantitative sense is provokingly unconcerned about those checks, because he has to know in the first place what his margin of error is.

BEUTEL: You go out and find out how many people want to buy Philco radios. That is one of the big problems of the commercial companies, I suppose. You get an answer from your sample. Now how could you possibly know *in advance* how many people wanted to buy Philco radios? There wouldn't be any sense in taking the whole test if it were known.

DEMING: I repeat, that in a quantitatively designed sample the margin of error is known, is computable and controllable in advance.

BEUTEL: How could it be known?

POLITZ: Perhaps it would be of some help to consider your particular problem about how many people want to buy Philco radios. We might say we are confronted with two major sources of error. One is, Do you go to the right people in your sampling so that you can project your findings to the total universe? If you went to atypical people, then you admit the figures have no value. Let us call it a problem of sampling.

BEUTEL: That is clear enough. But I want to know how you know after they tell you that they want a Philco radio that they are not, let's say, lying to you?

POLITZ: Either they tell you something that is not true, or actually believe something different from the truth. If we ask people "What will you buy when the war is over?" we find 25 per cent of the population is going to buy airplanes. We can demonstrate your point on that matter.

In reference to the question "How can it be checked?" I don't think it can. I think we just have to wait a year and find out if the survey is right.

BEUTEL: Do you have the machinery for such a check? You report to a magazine, for example, that so many people want to subscribe. Do you have any way of going back and telling, when the magazine is put on the market, that the predicted number actually bought it?

POLITZ: Let's stick to the Philco example, for clarity's sake. If you ask the question "Will you buy a Philco radio?"—the mere fact the question is related to the future, does not give us any chance to check it; we simply have to wait.

If we ask, "Will you buy a radio within a year?" and get the answer, all we can do is wait for the year and see if the survey is right or wrong. All we can say then, in the way of any applied science, is that if the technique used in this survey gave us the wrong answer as checked by the development, let us not use it again. Perhaps, and most likely, the technique might be wrong in other respects too.

You might ask a different question of Miss Ellis. She deals with present problems. For instance, she might try to find out who reads her magazine, and since reading is something we cannot observe, and on the other hand is not related to the future, your question might be, "Did you read it?" Therefore we have a better way of arriving at a result because the human error might not be so great, so long as people tell us the truth.

How can we tell if they told us the truth? Several ways. For instance if you suspect, as I have, that their endeavor to show up well might make them mention a certain type of magazine instead of the other one, we have an "inflationary" force. But we might have a way of checking it. As Mr. Crossley suggested a while ago, if you cannot remove people's intention to show off, you can at least measure the intention by showing the magazine before it actually came out. If for instance, before the magazine was published six per cent tell you they have read it before, then you know that there is an inflation of about six per cent. That would be one way.

But still, to go all the way with you: that helps only in one respect, because although we remove inflation there are other magazines that suffer from understatement. Nothing helps us there. If somebody denies reading it, that is of course the end of the research. But then again we might try the technique of switching questions. If you know that intention to lie has to do with showing off, you might switch to a technique in which you have a chance to make an objective check. I would ask "Did you buy it?" and if you come out with the right number of copies sold, you have a check on the validity of the subject.

ELLIS: In answer to Dr. Beutel, one of the techniques we have used consists of questioning the girl in the home separately. We are interested in knowing if any of the girls do the food shopping for the family. We thought it would help us to check the answers by asking the mothers separately. We used the same method concerning the question of expenditure for clothes. We believed the teen-ager would tend to exaggerate what she paid for a coat, let's say. So we thought of having the mother check the answers.

DEMING: The most important part of any survey, or the part that takes 90 per cent of the time in the preparation, is how to ask the question. That part has to be worked out, even if the survey is to be a complete count. If the job cannot be done on a complete basis, you can't do it on the sample basis.

As for reliability, I was speaking of the reliability of the sample in comparison with what you would have got on complete coverage. That sampling error, or the range within which the sampling error will lie, must be known in advance. Whether or not the answer is good depends on the training of the interviewer and must be worked out as if done on a complete basis. But I prefer that Dr. Guttman speak on that point.

GUTTMAN: I was just about to rise to suggest an example that is interesting in this question where a questionnaire was successfully able to predict what people would do a year hence.

In the army the research branch had been making surveys for the last four or five years. One of the problems put to them three years ago was how many soldiers would go back to school after the war was over. A survey was made, a full series of questions was asked, and they used the cross-scale analysis which I am going to discuss this afternoon. The study of the answers showed a minimum of seven per cent would go back if there was no government aid. If there was government aid, it was hard to get an upper statement, but it was between 30 and 35 per cent. After the G. I. Bill had been passed the survey was continued. Many soldiers are not clear as to the provisions of the bill. The minimum estimate was raised to 8 per cent and the maximum was around 20 or 25 per cent. The schools had plenty of warning as to how many were coming back.

BLANKENSHIP: Before we close this meeting, I should like to clear up a point of view of mine. I did not intend to give the impression that this technique of ours is a science. I am definitely on the other side of the issue. I think the analogy to the physician is a happy choice because I do not think myself that any medical man thinks he is a scientist. He practises an art and I think, in essence, that is what we do in the matter of measuring consumer preferences. Ours is an Art. We can, or are trying to, apply scientific principles as best we know how. Certainly in sampling we come closer to a science than perhaps in any other techniques, and I do think we are beginning to approach some scientific principles. If and when we come out with a final list of principles, we can evaluate our work. I am disappointed, in a way, that so much of our discussion got into the technical field, because I think it leaves us with an unbalanced point of view toward the aim of science. We got, for example, into a discussion of sampling. Then we got into the case of the various kinds of census. Actually I do not see, except for the specialized problem of sampling, that the matter of the census really should have played a role in our discussion. The so-called mass study is only one technique. The mass study of the consumer preferences, unfortunately, we devoted a very small amount of time to. Then, too, we have the whole consumer problem.

As far as I am concerned, I think that the question of whether research is a science is one of our standards for which to strive. Any one who is now practising research and claims he is in a science should, I think, be struck off the list immediately. So I am sorry we did not have a chance to get into some of the other criteria of scientific method.

WAYS OF EVALUATING PREFERENCES

CHAIRMAN: J. Parker Bursk, *University of Pennsylvania.*
SPEAKERS: L. L. Thurstone, *Department of Psychology, University of Chicago;* Francis W. Irwin, *Department of Psychology. University of Pennsylvania;* Louis Guttman, *Department of Sociology, Cornell University*

THE PREDICTION OF CHOICE
By
L. L. THURSTONE

WE SHALL describe first some special cases to illustrate the nature of the problem and we shall develop several psychophysical theorems in the prediction of choice and a method of computation.

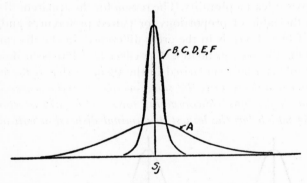

FIG. 1

As an example, let there be six psychological objects which may be as many candidates for elective office. To simplify the situation in this special case, let all of the six candidates be equally popular, on the average, so that their scale positions on the subjective continuum are all the same, namely, S_j, as shown in Figure 1. Let us assume that candidate A does or says something by which a thousand people become his enthusiastic supporters and that, at the same time, another thousand people hate him. Let this process continue in such a manner that the first candidate attains a large discriminal dispersion whereas the other candidates, B, C, D, E, F, retain their small discriminal dispersions. It is assumed in this example that the mean subjective values S_j remain the same during the campaign.

Before considering what will happen at the election, let us suppose that the six names are presented to the subjects in pairs where each candidate is paired with every other candidate. Such a list contains $n(n-1)/2 = 15$ pairs of names. The voters check their preferences for each pair of names. From such returns we can make a square table of proportions of judgments, $p_{j>k}$, to show the proportion of the voters who prefer j to k for every pair of names. In the present situation we should find that all of the proportions would be exactly the same, so that $p_{j>k} = .50$. In other words, the table of proportions of preference would show all of the six candidates to be equal in average popularity since their scale positions S_j are all the same.

Now, having the relations of Figure 1, or their numerical equivalents, the problem is to predict what the voters will do when they record their first choices for the six names. From the diagram, it is evident that the first candidate will get half of the votes and that the other five candidates will divide the other half. Hence we should expect the following division of the votes: .50; .10; .10; .10; .10; .10. The first candidate would have at least a plurality. The reason for the apparent discrepancy between the table of proportions for paired preferences and the prediction of first choice is in the great differences in the discriminal dispersions for the six candidates. The effect that has been described in this example can be summarized in the theorem that *if three or more psychological objects with the same average affective value and with symmetric dispersions are competing for selection as first choice, then the object which has the largest discriminal dispersion will obtain the*

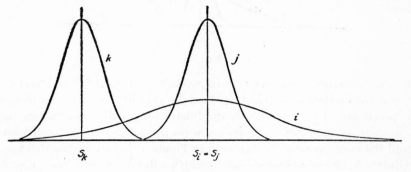

FIG. 2

largest number of votes. The effect which is here stated in terms of psychophysical concepts is no doubt known to practical politicians and perhaps to advertisers and to students of consumer preference. With the development of a theoretical structure for psychological measurement from the more restricted methods of traditional psychophysics we should have frequent contacts between theory and the intuitions of experience in practical affairs if our scientific rationalizations of social phenomena are sound.

Another example will now be described. Let Figure 2 represent the frequency distributions of two leading candidates, i and j, and let them have the same average affective value $S_i = S_j$. Assume that these distributions are Gaussian on the subjective continuum with different dispersions so that $\sigma_i > \sigma_j$ as shown in the figure. In this situation we should expect that the two candidates would draw the same number of votes so that it would be a matter of chance which of them actually became the winner. Now let us introduce a dark horse in the third candidate k whose scale value S_k is lower than that of the two leading candidates. This situation can be considered under two cases, namely, (1) the case in which the distributions of j and k do not overlap, and (2) the case in which the distributions j and k do overlap. The first case is shown in Figure 2.

Before the candidate k is introduced, the expectation is a tie between candidates i and j. After the introduction of candidate k, the expectation remains unaltered because the entire distribution for j exceeds the entire distribution for k. Hence *with no overlapping of* j *and* k, *the expectation is that candidate* k *gets no votes at all.* The expected vote is then the same as if the third candidate had not been introduced.

Case 2 is different as shown in Figure 3. Here there is an overlap between the less variable j of the two leading candidates and the candidate k. Most of those who perceive i in the lower half of the affective range

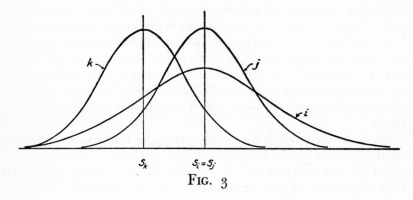

$$S_k \qquad S_i = S_j$$
FIG. 3

have the preference $j > i$. If some of them shift their first choices to k, the result will be a larger decrement in the votes for j than for i. Therefore the expectation is that i will have a plurality. We can summarize this situation in several theorems. *If two candidates have equal average affective values* $(S_i = S_j)$ *and different dispersions* $(\sigma_i > \sigma_j)$, *and if there is a third candidate with lower scale value and overlapping dispersion, there will be a plurality for the more variable of the two leading candidates. In the case of a threatened tie between two leading candidates, the more variable of the two candidates can win the election by introducing a less popular candidate.* This is a curious result. Perhaps this effect is also known to practical politicians. A limiting case is that in which the average popularity (S_k) of the third candidate is equal to that of i and j. Then, if i is still the most variable in affective dispersion, he wins the plurality. This case is covered by the first theorem. These theorems are not intended to be exhaustive. They are presented primarily for the purpose of indicating the potentialities of the concept of discriminal dispersion in the prediction of conduct. The subject sketched by these examples can be extended analytically into one of considerable proportions.

In voting for a first choice in a set of names, physical objects, or ideas, the subject sometimes encounters one or more objects that are complete strangers to him. He may even omit such candidates from consideration. In listing the distributions for computation of first choice we have then a reduced frequency for the active preference votes for this object. The residual frequency can be recorded at any point on the affective continuum below the active distributions of the other candidates.

ANALYTICAL METHOD

We turn now to a more formal consideration of the problem. A method of computation will be described which covers both of two general cases, namely, (1) that in which the affective dispersions are Gaussian, and (2) that in which the affective dispersions take any form, including bimodality which is characteristic of the latter phase of a political campaign. The computations will normally be based on experimental data obtained by the method of successive intervals. This psychophysical method will be described in improved form in a separate paper.

We begin the analysis with two overlapping Gaussian distributions on the affective continuum as illustrated in Figure 4. These two distributions represent two stimuli, i and j, with scale values S_i and S_j and with discriminal dispersions σ_i and σ_j. The distributions will be as-

sumed to be drawn with unit area so that their ordinates may be interpreted directly as probabilities with any suitable class intervals. The
probability that any percipient will experience stimulus i at any speci-

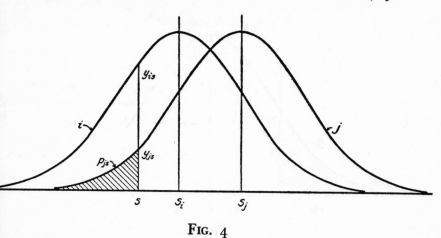

FIG. 4

fied affective value s is then the ordinate of the probability curve y_{is}
at the point s. The probability that the same percipient will experience
stimulus j at some value lower than s is then

$$p_{js} = \int_{-\infty}^{s} y_{js}\, ds , \qquad (1)$$

which is represented by the shaded area of Figure 4. Assuming that these
probabilities are independent, we have

$$P_{i>j} = \int_{-\infty}^{+\infty} y_{is}\, p_{js}\, ds , \qquad (2)$$

where $P_{i>j}$ is the probability that i will be perceived higher than j, irre-
spective of where i is perceived. The values of $P_{i>j}$ are, in fact, the experimentally given values in the method of paired comparison in which
each stimulus is compared separately with every other stimulus. This
method implies $n(n - 1)/2$ comparisons if each stimulus is not compared with itself and if the space or time orders ij and ji are not differentiated experimentally. When that is done, we have $n(n - 1)$ comparisons, and when we include the comparison of each stimulus with itself,
as is possible when the stimuli are defined in such a manner that their
individual identities are not recognized by the subject, then we have n^2
comparisons for the method of paired comparison in its complete form.
When only one of the stimuli is chosen as a standard for comparison
with each of the other stimuli, then we have the constant method with

n or $(n - 1)$ comparisons. The constant method of traditional psycho-physics is a special case of the more fundamental paired comparison method. The analysis so far is that of the law of comparative judgment

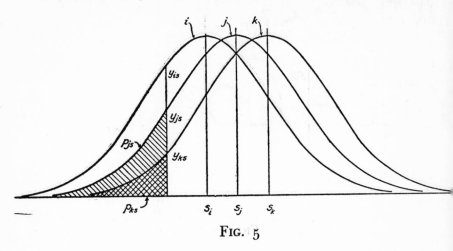

FIG. 5

which has been described in previous publications, but we are here concerned with the obverse problem of predicting behavior when S_j and σ_j are known.

Let us now consider a set of three overlapping affective distributions. Let the three stimuli be denoted i, j, and k as shown in Figure 5. As before, the probability that i will be perceived at s is y_{is}. The probability that j will be perceived below s is p_{js}, which is the single cross-hatched area. The probability that k will be perceived below s is p_{ks} which is the double cross-hatched area. Assuming, as before, that the probabilities are independent we have

$$P_{i.1} = \int_{-\infty}^{+\infty} y_{is}\, p_{js}\, p_{ks}\, ds \,, \tag{3}$$

where $P_{i.1}$ is the probability that the stimulus i will be selected as first choice when all three stimuli are presented. If there are N individuals we should have

$$N P_{i.1} = E_{i.1}, \tag{4}$$

where $E_{i.1}$ is the expected number of votes for stimulus i when all three stimuli are presented for selection of one stimulus by each subject.

Instead of dealing with continuous distributions we can restate the same relations in summational form for a set of frequencies in successive intervals. Let the affective continuum be divided into s successive intervals $1, 2, 3, \dots, m, \dots s$, where m denotes the general interval. It should be noted explicitly that these intervals need *not* be equal, as is illustrated in Figure 6. In fact, the method of successive intervals is a psychophysical method in which the intervals are not ordinarily equal. Their magnitudes can be determined for each set of observations. However, the problem of prediction of choice can be solved without even knowing the relative sizes of the successive class intervals.

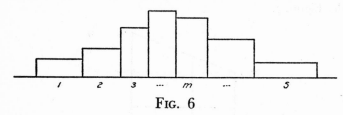

FIG. 6

Let f_{im} denote the frequency with which the stimulus i is perceived in the interval m so that

$$\sum_m f_{im} = N_i = N,\tag{5}$$

where N is the number of experimental subjects who perceived and classified the stimulus i. The corresponding relative frequency is then

$$\frac{1}{N} f_{im} = y_{im}\tag{6}$$

in the class intervals m, so that y_{im} is the probability that the stimulus i will be perceived in the affective interval m.

Let the stimulus i be the one about which we want to predict the number of first choices. Let each of the other stimuli be denoted k. Then $P_{i.1}$ will denote the proportion of subjects who vote for the stimulus i as their first choice in comparison with the whole group k.

The probability that any one of the stimuli k will be perceived below any specified class interval m is then

$$p_{k[m-1]} = \sum_{t=1}^{m=1} y_{kt} = p_{k<m},\tag{7}$$

where t denotes successive intervals. The summation is here over $(m-1)$ intervals, since $P_{k<m}$ denotes the probability that any stimulus k will be perceived *below* the interval m. Since we want to determine the probability that the stimulus i will be perceived higher than all of the stimuli in group k, we must deal with the whole group k. The probability that all of the $(n-1)$ stimuli k will be perceived below any designated class interval m is the product of the $(n-1)$ probabilities $p_{k[m-1]}$. Denoting this product $u_{[m-1]}$ we have

$$u_{m-1} \equiv p_{1[m-1]} p_{2[m-1]} \cdots p_{k[m-1]} \cdots p_{[n-1][m-1]} = \prod_{k=1}^{n-1} p_{k[m-1]}.\tag{8}$$

If we take the product $y_{im}\, u(m-1)$, we have the probability that the stimulus i is perceived in the interval m and that all of the stimuli in group k are perceived below the interval m. To sum this product for all the intervals would not give the desired answer because when the stimulus i is perceived in interval m, it may exceed one or more of the stimuli k which are also perceived in the same interval. To cover this situation consider Figure 7.

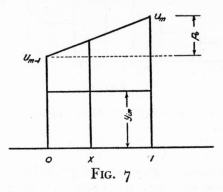

FIG. 7

In Figure 7 we have a class interval which is here given the range 0 to 1 as shown. Let y_{im} be the probability that stimulus i is perceived in the interval m. This ordinate is drawn in the figure as in a histogram so that we are assuming a rectangular distribution within each interval. The ordinate u_m is the probability that all of the stimuli in group k are perceived below the top of the interval m. Then

$$u_m = p_{1m} \cdot p_{2m} \cdot p_{3m} \cdots p_{km} \cdots p_{[n-1]m} = \prod_{k=1}^{n-1} p_{km}. \qquad (9)$$

The corresponding probability for the bottom of the same class interval is given by equation (8). Let x be any point in the class interval m as in the figure. The probability that stimulus i is perceived at the point x is $(y_{im}\, dx)$ and the probability that, at the same time, all of the stimuli in group k are perceived below x is $(u_{m-1} + xp_0)$, where

$$p_0 = (u_m - u_{m-1}). \qquad (10)$$

Hence we have

$$P_{im>k} = \int_0^1 y_{im}\,(u_{m-1} + xp_0)\, dx = y_{im}\, u_{m-1} + \tfrac{1}{2}\, y_{im}\, p_0, \qquad (11)$$

which is the probability that i is perceived in the interval m and that all of the group k are perceived below i. The desired probability $P_{i,1}$ that i

will be an individual voter's first choice is the summation of $P_{im>k}$ for all intervals m. Expressing p_o in terms of the u's, we have

$$p_{i.1} = \tfrac{1}{2} \sum_{m=1}^{s} y_{im}(u_m + u_{m-1}) . \tag{12}$$

This summation can also be written in the form

$$P_{i.1} = \tfrac{1}{2} \sum_{m=1}^{s} [y_{im} + y_{i[m+1]}] \, u_m = \tfrac{1}{2} \sum_{m=1}^{s} z_{im} \, u_m , \tag{13}$$

where

$$z_{im} = y_{im} + y_{i[m+1]} . \tag{14}$$

It should be recalled that this prediction of first choice for any given stimulus i can be made even though the class intervals remain unknown as to their relative magnitudes. Further, this computing formula has no restriction as to the shapes of the affective distributions. Several of them might be skewed while others are bimodal. A reservation about this computing formula is that it assumes independent probabilities. In dealing with affective discrimination for a large class of psychological objects this assumption is valid. If the affective deviations of a pair of objects are correlated, then the analysis becomes more complex. It can be made in terms of experimental data for the method of successive intervals. When the psychophysical problem is concerned with repeated judgments by the same individual, then the assumption of independence is valid except when the experimental situation introduces affective contrast or related effects. These can usually be avoided with good experimental procedures.

NUMERICAL EXAMPLES

In Table 1 we have tabulated the distributions for three stimuli on the affective continuum as they might be found from the experimental method of successive intervals. Here we have chosen arbitrary bimodal and skewed distributions to illustrate the latitude of the method. In this problem it is not necessary to evaluate the relative sizes of these intervals. They are denoted merely as successive intervals from 1 to 9, inclusive. The number of intervals is arbitrary. The probabilities y_{1m}, y_{2m}, y_{3m}, are listed as shown. Next we compute the corresponding values of p_{jm}. These summations are made from the lowest intervals so that the value of p_{jm} for $m = 9$ is unity for each stimulus j.

The values of u_{jm} are next recorded. For example, the value for u_{1m} in the interval $m = 2$ is $p_{2m}p_{3m} = .16 \times .02 = .0032$. In the next three columns we list the values of z_m. For example, the entry z_{3m} for $m = 5$ is $(.34 + .14) = .48$.

CONSUMER INTEREST

TABLE 1

m	y_1	y_2	y_3	p_1	p_2	p_3	u_1	u_2	u_3	z_1	z_2	z_3
1	.04	.03	.00	.04	.03	.00	.0000	.0000	.0012	.20	.16	.02
2	.16	.13	.02	.20	.16	.02	.0032	.0040	.0320	.29	.31	.16
3	.13	.18	.14	.33	.34	.16	.0544	.0528	.1122	.24	.35	.48
4	.11	.17	.34	.44	.51	.50	.2550	.2200	.2244	.19	.32	.68
5	.08	.15	.34	.52	.66	.84	.5544	.4368	.3432	.14	.27	.48
6	.06	.12	.14	.58	.78	.98	.7644	.5684	.4524	.17	.22	.16
7	.11	.10	.02	.69	.88	1.00	.8800	.6900	.6072	.30	.18	.02
8	.19	.08	.00	.88	.96	1.00	.9600	.8800	.8448	.31	.12	.00
9	.12	.04	.00	1.00	1.00	1.00	1.0000	1.0000	1.0000	.12	.04	.00

i	$2P$	P
1	.9516	.47
2	.6029	.30
3	.4609	.23
	2.0154	1.00

The final step is to sum the cross products $z_{jm}u_{jm}$. The sums give values of $2P_{j.1}$. These are listed separately in the table. The result gives 47% of the votes for the first stimulus, 30% for the second stimulus, and 23% for the third. An adjustment of less than 1% is indicated in the summation. This discrepancy is due to the assumed linearity of the function u within each class interval. It is small for a large number of class intervals.

In Table 2 we have a numerical example of the theorem that when two psychological objects are tied in average popularity, as measured by the mean scale positions S_i and S_j, then the more variable of them can win election for first choice by the introduction of a third competing object of lower average popularity. Here we used 24 successive intervals. All three of these affective distributions were made Gaussian, and it is here assumed that the distributions are at least roughly symmetric. The first two candidates are the leading ones that are tied. The third candidate has a lower average popularity as shown in the columns y_{im}, y_{jm}, y_{km}. The computations are similar to those of the previous example and we have the following results:

Expected votes for only two
    candidates: $i = 50\%; j = 50\%$
Expected votes after introducing new
    candidate: $i = 48\%; j = 45\%; k = 7\%$.

Here the more variable candidate i has obtained a plurality by introducing a new candidate with lower average popularity.

TABLE 2

m	y_1	y_2	y_3	p_1	p_2	p_3	u_1	u_2	u_3	z_1	z_2	z_3
1	.00	.00	.00	.00	.00	.00	.0000	.0000	.0000	.01	.00	.00
2	.01	.00	.00	.01	.00	.00	.0000	.0000	.0000	.01	.00	.00
3	.00	.00	.00	.01	.00	.00	.0000	.0000	.0000	.01	.00	.01
4	.01	.00	.01	.02	.00	.01	.0000	.0002	.0000	.03	.00	.02
5	.02	.00	.01	.04	.00	.02	.0000	.0008	.0000	.05	.00	.06
6	.03	.00	.05	.07	.00	.07	.0000	.0049	.0000	.07	.01	.14
7	.04	.01	.09	.11	.01	.16	.0016	.0176	.0011	.09	.02	.24
8	.05	.01	.15	.16	.02	.31	.0062	.0496	.0032	.12	.06	.34
9	.07	.05	.19	.23	.07	.50	.0350	.1150	.0161	.15	.14	.38
10	.08	.09	.19	.31	.16	.69	.1104	.2139	.0496	.17	.24	.34
11	.09	.15	.15	.40	.31	.84	.2604	.3360	.1240	.19	.34	.24
12	.10	.19	.09	.50	.50	.93	.4650	.4650	.2500	.20	.38	.14
13	.10	.19	.05	.60	.69	.98	.6762	.5880	.4140	.19	.34	.06
14	.09	.15	.01	.69	.84	.99	.8316	.6831	.5796	.17	.24	.02
15	.08	.09	.01	.77	.93	1.00	.9300	.7700	.7161	.15	.14	.01
16	.07	.05	.00	.84	.98	1.00	.9800	.8400	.8232	.12	.06	.00
17	.05	.01	.00	.89	.99	1.00	.9900	.8900	.8811	.09	.02	.00
18	.04	.01	.00	.93	1.00	1.00	1.0000	.9300	.9300	.07	.01	.00
19	.03	.00	.00	.96	1.00	1.00	1.0000	.9600	.9600	.05	.00	.00
20	.02	.00	.00	.98	1.00	1.00	1.0000	.9800	.9800	.03	.00	.00
21	.01	.00	.00	.99	1.00	1.00	1.0000	.9900	.9900	.01	.00	.00
22	.00	.00	.00	.99	1.00	1.00	1.0000	.9900	.9900	.01	.00	.00
23	.01	.00	.00	1.00	1.00	1.00	1.0000	1.0000	1.0000	.01	.00	.00
24	.00	.00	.00	1.00	1.00	1.00	1.0000	1.0000	1.0000	.00	.00	.00

		$2P$	P
i	1	.9634	.48
j	2	.9109	.45
k	3	.1327	.07
		2.0070	1.00

The examples have been limited to groups of two or three objects but the theory can be extended to groups of any size. For large groups, the computational procedure can be rearranged in a more economical manner.

IMPLICATIONS OF DISCRIMINAL DISPERSION

While the examples of this paper have referred to political elections, the psychophysical theory is applicable to the comparison and ranking of psychological objects of any kind. Since it is a major purpose of this paper to indicate some analytical and experimental implications of the concept of discriminal dispersion, it may be in order to mention briefly its relations to psychological measurement of several kinds of objects.

First, consider the formal laboratory measurement of sensory and perceptual functions. In measuring pitch discrimination we can get along with the traditional psychophysical methods if we use stimuli that are carefully controlled so as to be quite homogeneous in all but the attribute to be discriminated. But suppose we want to study pitch discrimination under wide variations in timbre, including noises. Then the stimuli are not homogeneous in other attributes and they will almost certainly differ widely in discriminal dispersion. It would still be possible to measure pitch discrimination under such variant conditions and the individual differences so found might be of considerable psychological and physiological interest. The older psychophysical methods would then be inadequate. The discriminal dispersions as well as the scale values can be determined from complete paired comparison data if the stimuli cover a supraliminal range in pitch.

In the measurement of social attitudes of a group it is not only the average affective value of a proposal or idea that is of significance but also the dispersion of affective values within the group. It may even be possible to *define the morale of a group in terms of the sum of affective dispersions of all its debatable issues.* The effects of propaganda are no doubt determined in part by the heterogeneity of affective values which are themselves to be altered by propaganda. Moral values are essentially affective in nature. The moral code of a social group can be described by its affective values in which the highest ones are what the group considers to be sacred. Measurement of the seriousness of crimes can be made by psychophysical methods in which the dispersions are signs of heterogeneity or lack of unity in the group and its code.

Studies have been made of international attitudes by asking the subjects to rate their preferences for nationalities in pairs. If some of the subjects are given the question "Which of these two nationalities would you rather associate with?" and if others are asked the question "Which of these two nationalities would you rather have your sister marry?" the results will be essentially the same as regards rank order with a linear relation between the two sets of scale values for the nationalities. But the dispersions will be widely different, showing greater discrimination for the second question than for the first. This is what we should expect. It is another example in which social judgments are represented in part by the discriminal dispersions with effects that are not always so obvious as in this example.

International attitudes can be studied with the psychophysical methods. This was done with newspaper editorials for the period 1910 to 1930, which included the period of World War I. The analysis showed the rate of decline of editorial attitudes toward Germany and the rise of attitude toward France and the later recovery of pre-war attitudes. It seems likely that if such studies were made in a manner to reveal the group dispersions as well as the scale values, the result might be a rather sensitive barometer of increasing heterogeneity in international attitudes. Rapid changes in scale values or in group dispersions would be signals of impending crises.

The measurement of consumer preferences should be done by psychophysical methods that yield central tendencies and group dispersions as two parameters for each object. The experimental methods are easily used and they can yield predictions of relative consumption of competing commodities.

In the measurement of utility the psychologists and the economists are dealing with overlapping problems. The utility concept is essentially the same as that of mean affective value for the individual. The addition of a parameter for dispersion could lead to interesting results for psychological and economic theory. Consider, for example, a surface whose base coördinates represent amount of two commodities and whose ordinates represent the associated utility or affective value for the individual. Horizontal sections of this surface give a family of indifference curves whereas vertical sections, parallel to either base axis, give satisfaction curves which are interpreted as Fechner's law. Now, if the dispersions in affective values among the individuals are introduced as new parameters, we have the possibility of summing the effects for the individuals to that of the group. Further, *the first derivative of the satisfaction curve at any point is the motivation of the invdividual* with reference to the commodity concerned.

The application of psychophysical methods in experimental aesthetics is well known. The addition of a parameter for group dispersion would be indicative of the heterogeneity of aesthetic criteria for each object. Aesthetic theory is often regarded as a subject to be settled by scholarly debate or by reference to Aristotle. It would be better to test aesthetic theory by reference to experimental methods that are available. We could then find out where Aristotle guessed right and where he guessed wrong. Here we are assuming that aesthetics is not normative. We assume that the aesthetic value of an object is determined by what goes on in the mind of the percipient. What is an aesthetic object for one percipient is prosaic to another. In a homogeneous culture, it should be possible by experimental means to describe, and even to measure, those object attributes which have aesthetic value for most individuals in that culture.

The purpose of the psychophysical methods is to allocate each one of a set of psychological objects to the subjective continuum which is also called the discriminal continuum. Measurement in this continuum is effected with *a subjective unit of measurement,* namely, *the discriminal error,* with criteria for internal consistency that differentiate measurement from mere rank order. The psychological objects may be any objects or ideas about which the subject can make comparative judgments in the form "A is x'er than B," where x is any designated attribute. When each psychological object j has been allocated, it is described by two parameters, namely, its mean scale position S_j and the discriminal dispersion σ_j which the stimulus projects on the subjective continuum. The purpose of this paper has been to consider the obverse problem of predicting the behavior of the subjects in terms of these parameters. In particular we wanted to predict the relative frequency with which the subjects select any designated object as their first choice.

William James said that psychophysics was the dullest part of psychology. He was right. But if we extend and adapt the psychophysical concepts to the theory of discriminatory and selective judgment, the subject takes a different color and it is no longer dull.

THE CASE OF PREDICTION WITH CORRELATED RATINGS

In the previous sections of this paper the writer has presented several psychophysical theorems concerning the problem of predicting how many people will select any given stimulus as their first choice when the scale values and discriminal dispersions are known for each stimulus. Those theorems were written with the explicit reservation that they assumed independent probabilities, i.e., they assumed the scale values of the stimuli to be uncorrelated. In practice it is to be expected that the scale values will be correlated for many types of preferential judgments, and it is desirable, therefore, to devise methods of prediction of choice that are free from this restrictive assumption. Here we shall describe a method of prediction of choice which is independent of the shapes of the affective distributions and also independent of their intercorrelations.

The problem is, then, to predict the proportion of voters (or buyers) who will select any particular psychological object (person, idea, or thing) as their first choice in a group of such objects. It will be assumed that there is available a random and representative sample of individuals from the population about which the prediction is to be made. It will be assumed that we want to determine the scale values and discriminal dispersions of a large *collection* of objects but that the actual presentation to the total population will be a smaller *group* of such objects. Let the large collection contain N objects or stimuli which will be referred to as the *collection*. Let the smaller group to be presented to the total population contain u objects which will be referred to as the *group* of stimuli. The reason for this formulation is that it may be desirable to select the group of stimuli for selection by the population on the basis of information concerning relative popularity and dispersions of a large collection of objects. When these are known, the smaller group can be selected with foresight as to the desired objectives. For example, the stimulus collection may consist in a set of principles and we may want to predict which set or group of these principles can be combined into a proposal that the population will accept with a majority endorsement. This requires a labeled neutral point in the method of successive intervals. Or the stimulus group may consist of ten neckties whose patterns and colors should be so selected from a large collection as to maximize acceptance by the population. The scale values and dispersions may be examined to select the most appropriate smaller combination which shall constitute the stimulus group for general presentation.

If each individual may select one necktie, then the group of neckties should be so assembled from the available collection as to maximize the scale values *of those which are rated as first choices.* This solution is not the same as that of assembling a group of stimuli with the highest scale values. Such a group may please a number of individuals with more than one stimulus of their favorite kinds while others remain disappointed. The problems in this area are not only of theoretical interest in the adaptation of psychophysics to practical affairs. Their solutions may also bear interesting relations to problems of social theory.

The experimental procedure is to ask each subject to place each stimulus in one of seven successive categories. The procedure is superficially similar to that of the method of equal appearing intervals but there is an important difference in the instructions to the subject. In the method of equal appearing intervals, the subject is asked to place the stimuli in the several piles so that they seem to him to be about equally spaced as to the attribute in which the stimuli are being rated. It can be shown experimentally that the subject is unable to carry out such instructions and that in fact the intervals toward the ends are greater than the intervals in the middle range. In the method of successive intervals, we do not impose any such restriction. The successive intervals are either given successive numbers, 1, 2, 3, etc., or they are given descriptive names. When the successive classes are identified by descriptive phrases, the wording should be carefully done so that the subjects accept immediately the successive nature of the categories. If the subjects object that the labels on the successive classes are out of sequence, then the experimental procedure fails. It is usually rather easy to designate the successive categories in such a way that their order is accepted by all of the subjects. They then proceed to place each stimulus in one of the classes according to the labels without any restriction that the intervals shall be in any sense equal. There is of course no restriction as to the shape of the distribution of judgments in this successive interval classification. Occasionally, students of psychology need to be reminded that the normal distribution of categories has nothing to do with this case.

The computational procedure is rather simple. For each subject we record the particular stimuli that he rated in the highest category which he used. In addition we record the number of stimuli in that category. This category need not be the highest in the set because a subject may leave blank one or more of the upper categories. It is the highest category in which he rated any stimuli.

From these basic data we tabulate n_{jm}, which is the number of subjects who placed stimulus j in the highest category in a group of m stimuli that were rated in the same category. The highest category is not necessarily the same for all subjects. Thus n_{j_3} means the number of subjects who placed j in their highest class and who placed a total of three stimuli in that class.

In estimating the number of subjects who would rate stimulus j as their first choice we make several plausible assumptions. First, we assume that those who rated j in their highest interval or category and who placed all other stimuli in lower classes would be expected to rate j as their first choice. Further, we assume that those who placed j and one other stimulus k in the highest interval would divide their votes for first choice between j and k with equal frequencies. Similarly, those who placed j in the highest interval together with a total of m stimuli in that interval would also divide evenly their selections for first choice among the m stimuli. This assumption is not quite correct, but it is very nearly so if the total number of categories is not too small. Theoretically one could differentiate among the m stimuli in the highest class by the shapes of the frequency distributions, treating them as continuous frequency curves rather than as histograms, but such a correction is probably not worth the trouble in most practical work.

These assumptions lead to an estimation formula which can be written in the form

$$N_{j_1} = n_{j_1} + \frac{1}{2} n_{j_2} + \frac{1}{3} n_{j_3} + \cdots + \frac{1}{m} n_{jm} + \cdots + \frac{1}{t} n_{jt}, \qquad (15)$$

where

$N_{j_1} =$ number of subjects who give stimulus j their first choice,

$t =$ largest number of stimuli which any subject put in his highest interval.

Summing, we have

$$N_{j_1} = \sum_{m=1}^{t} \left(\frac{n_{jm}}{m} \right),$$

which applies to each stimulus in turn.

The experimental procedure contemplates the sorting by each subject of a relatively large number of stimuli into a relatively small number of successive categories. This procedure is feasible, whereas it is not feasible to ask a subject to put, say, 50 or 100 stimuli in rank order. From the data for the sortings into a rather small number of categories, say seven, one can estimate the number of subjects who would give their first choice to any particular stimulus j when this stimulus is presented with any particular combination of other stimuli in the collection.

Several psychophysical methods and concepts have been described in previous papers by the author. Some of these papers are listed below.

REFERENCES

1. Thurstone, L. L. Equally often noticed differences. *J. educ. Psychol,* 1927, *18,* 289–93.
2. ———. A law of comparative judgment. *Psychol. Rev.,* 1927, *34,* 273–86.
3. ———. Psychophysical analysis. *Amer. J. Psychol.,* 1927, *38,* 368–89.
4. ———. A mental unit of measurement. *Psychol. Rev.,* 1927, *34,* 415–23.
5. ———. Three psychophysical laws. *Psychol. Rev.,* 1927, *34,* 424–32.
6. ———. Experimental study of nationality preferences. *J. gen. Psychol.,* 1928, *1,* 405–25.
7. ———. Fechner's law and the method of equal appearing intervals. *J. exp. Psychol.,* 1929, *12,* 214–24.
8. ———. The indifference function. *J. soc. Psychol.,* 1931, 2, 139–67.
9. ———. Rank order as a psychophysical method. *J. exp. Psychol.,* 1931, *14,* 187–201.
10. ———. Ability, motivation, and speed. *Psychometrika,* 1937, 2, 249–54.

SOME SITUATIONAL EFFECTS
UPON PREFERENCES
By
FRANCIS W. IRWIN

THE data which are to be discussed here have been obtained in a series of experiments over the past several years. Our present interest in these experiments is not in their technical aspects; since we were invading a new field, the methods used were not on a highly developed technical level. Likewise we are not interested in the purely psychological significance of the results. Rather, we wish to extract from the data certain *experimental illustrations* of influences such as might appear in almost any study of preferences, and of which it would therefore be well for experimenters to be aware.

The experiments were originally suggested by the work of Herbert F. Wright,[1] who concluded, after an extensive series of studies, that interposing a physical or spatial barrier between a person and an object which is attractive to him tended to increase the attractiveness of the object, in accordance with the proverb, "Grass on the other side of the fence is greener." I shall not attempt here to evaluate Wright's conclusions, but shall proceed to discuss certain temporal, social, and other influences which we have found to play a part in the determination of preferences.

The first two points which I wish to illustrate are as follows:

1. Preferences are not determined simply by the usefulness of an object as perceived by an individual. It can easily be shown that what may be called "irrational" factors are present.

2. Preferences are not based simply upon the perceived characteristics of the objects as such; the context of the situation in which the preferences are expressed may be predominant.

For example, Armitt and Simon [2] set up an experiment in which children four to nine years of age were confronted by two toys, games, or other attractive objects appropriate to their age and sex. Each child was told that he would receive both of these objects, but that one of them, which was pointed out, would be given to him immediately, and the other he would receive one week or a few minutes later, as the case might be. (In all of the experiments which are to be reported upon, each object was used equally often for each of the alternative conditions.) The experimenter then asked the child, as casually as possible, which of the objects he liked the better. The results of these experiments showed a considerable preponderance of preferences for the object which the child was to receive immediately. In four experiments, the numbers of subjects who preferred the immediate object were 22 out of 25, 19 out of 25, 16 out of 25, and 18 out of 25. (No significant difference appeared between the three-minute and one-week intervals.) It may also be noted that, in some of these experiments, the children were not asked to state their preference verbally. Instead, the experimenter told the child to take whichever object he wanted to play with for a while, while the experimenter did some work at his desk. No significant difference appeared between these action choices and the verbal preferences of the other experiments.

[1] H. F. Wright, "The Influence of Barriers on the Strength of Motivation." *Contr. Psychol. Theor.*, 1937, 1, No. 3, pp. 143 f.

[2] F. W. Irwin, Fannie M. Armitt, and C. W. Simon, "Studies in object-preferences. I. The effect of temporal proximity." *J. Exp. Psychol.*, 1943, *33*, 64–72.

In order to determine whether this temporal influence could be discovered in adults, Orchinik and Weiss [3] carried out experiments on college students. To disguise the problem, they asked subjects to volunteer for an experiment and had them perform some task like cancellation or learning nonsense syllables, over a period of ten to fifteen minutes. The subject was then told that, while we could not offer to pay him for the service, he would be given two postcard-size reproductions of famous paintings. He was shown the two pictures and was told that he would receive one of them immediately, but that the other one, for one reason or another, would be given to him a week later. After engaging the subject in some casual conversation, the experimenter asked him which of the pictures he liked the better. In Weiss's experiment, 25 preferred the immediate picture, 11 the deferred picture, and 4 would not make a decision. In Orchinik's experiment, carried out a year later, 41 preferred the immediate picture, and 23 the deferred picture. Taking the two experiments together, a total of 66 subjects preferred the immediate picture and 34 the deferred one.

Gebhard [4] carried out a series of studies of certain social influences upon preferences. For example, she showed a child two objects appropriate to his age and sex, and told him that he would receive one of the objects, which was indicated, and that another child would receive the other. She then casually asked the child which he liked the better. In one of these experiments 25 out of 38 children expressed a preference for the object which they were to receive; in another, 28 out of 36 expressed a similar preference.

These data appear to indicate clearly that an expressed preference is by no means necessarily determined by either the perceived usefulness or the perceived stimulus characteristics of the objects. Such influences need to be kept in mind in work on preferences, since they may easily be introduced unawares.

3. As a third point, it may be observed that the factors we have studied can operate even when one of the objects involved in the comparison is not present to the senses. Thus Gebhard in some instances, using children five to eight years of age, showed a child an object and told him that this object was to be given to another child, while another object, which she had "forgotten" to bring with her, but which was mentioned by name, would be given to him. When the children were asked which they liked the better, 23 out of 36 stated that they preferred the one

[3] F. W. Irwin, C. W. Orchinik, and Johanna Weiss, "Studies in object-preferences. The effect of temporal proximity upon adults' preferences." *Amer. J. Psychol.*, 1946, *59*, 458-62.

[4] F. W. Irwin, and Mildred Gebhard, "Studies in object-preferences. The effect of ownership and other social influences." *Amer. J. Psychol.*, 1946, *59*, 633-51.

that they were to be given (even though it was not physically present). The experimenter then said, "Oh, I am sorry. I have made a mistake. We will have to begin all over again." She then took the child to the door, as if to make a fresh start, brought him back, and told him that *he* would receive the object which was shown, while another child would receive the object which was mentioned but was not present. Enough of the 36 children changed their preferences so that 23 of the 36 now said that they liked better the object which they were being given, and which was present.

4. A fourth point, which is offered somewhat tentatively, is that combined favorable influences may not operate additively. Evidence for this is as follows. Gebhard discovered that if the experimenter expressed her own preference for one of two objects, the children's preferences tended, to some extent, to be influenced favorably toward that object. Again, Gebhard found in several experiments (as mentioned above) that children tended to express a preference for an object which they were to receive, as compared with an object which another child was to receive. It therefore suggested itself that a very strong effect should be produced by combining these two influences in one situation. When this was done, however, no overwhelming effect occurred. The result gave a preponderance of preferences for the object favored both by the experimenter's own statement and by prospective ownership which was at most no greater than the effect produced by prospective ownership alone: out of 30 subjects, only 18 expressed a preference for the object which was favored by both influences. We do not consider this evidence to be final, since on various grounds the absolute values in these experiments are not to be taken too seriously. However, the data suggest, at least, that favorable influences need not combine additively.

5. As a fifth point, we have evidence that common sense is by no means a reliable guide to the prediction of such preferences as we were studying. When Gebhard's experiment concerning the effect of prospective ownership was described in detail to a class of 81 college students, and these students were asked in which direction they believed the majority of preferences would occur, two students made a prediction which agreed with the actual results, one was undecided, and 78 predicted the opposite of the actual event. It is indeed no new notion that experimentation, rather than common sense, is necessary to provide reliable basis for such predictions; but the very striking nature of the present illustration may be of some interest.

6. The sixth and final point is that an individual who expresses a preference need not be expected to be able to give the correct reason for his preference, if he is asked for it. For example, when Armitt and

Simon asked their subjects why they preferred one object to another, in the experiments in which the subjects were to receive one object immediately and the other later, the children made such replies as the following:

"Because I wanted it."
"It looked prettier."
"I want to wear it to the movies and church."
"Because I like to look at picture books."
"Just 'cause I wanted to."

Reasons offered by Gebhard's subjects, in her experiments on the effect of prospective ownership, can be illustrated as follows:

"I like to play cards better than marbles."
"Because I like airplanes."
"Because it would help more in school."
"The other is more for a little kid."

Orchinik's college-student subjects offered reasons for their preferences of one picture over another, in the experiment in which they were to receive one immediately and the other later, of which the following are typical:

"I do not like Renoir."
"I like blue."
"I am fond of that painting."
"It's a stronger painting."
"I like the blue dress."
"The other has too much detail."

In only a very small number of reasons, in any of these experiments, was there any observable reference to the experimental variable which was operative in the situation. There seems to be no reason to suppose that the subjects knew that they were being influenced by experimental variable, but wished to conceal this fact or to deceive the experimenter. In many instances, when the college students were informed of the nature and purpose of the experiment, they still took the attitude that perhaps the experimental variable operated on other subjects, but that they were not aware of its operating upon them. On the whole, we regard the outcome as further evidence, to be added to what psychologists have long known, that individuals are by no means necessarily aware of all of the influences which motivate them.

To summarize briefly, we have offered some experimental illustrations of the facts that preferences are wholly determined neither by the perceived usefulness of objects nor by the perceived stimulus characteristics of the objects as such; that what we may call "irrational" factors may prevail even when one of the two objects concerned is not present to the senses; that it is unsafe to assume that favorable influences will combine additively; that prediction of preferences cannot safely be made on the basis of common sense; and that preferences may be determined by factors of which the individual concerned is entirely unaware.

THE CORNELL TECHNIQUE FOR SCALE AND INTENSITY ANALYSIS

By

Louis Guttman

INTRODUCTION

DURING the course of the war, a new approach to the problem of scaling attitudes and public opinion, called *scalogram* analysis, was developed by the writer to aid in the study of the morale and related aspects of the United States Army. This approach has wide ramifications not only for attitude and opinion research, but for many other fields like market research, mental testing, and elsewhere where it is desired to quantify qualitative data. Not much has yet been published [1] on this approach during the five years it has been used by the Army, so that it has not been readily available to other research workers.

The work of the Research Branch of the Information and Education Division of the War Department, done under the scientific leadership of Professor Samuel A. Stouffer, will be described in several volumes now being completed. One of these volumes contains a rather comprehensive treatise on the theory and practice of scalogram analysis as carried out by the Research Branch.

The purpose of the present paper is to present another technique for scalogram analysis which can be used immediately by research workers. Justification for the technique follows from the general theory and evidence to be published in the forthcoming volumes on the Research Branch. We shall call it the *Cornell technique* for scalogram analysis to distinguish it from several alternative devices, since it was developed first for teaching purposes at Cornell. It is hoped that the reader can follow the technique through from only the present description. For fuller exposition of the theory, and discussion of problems of reliability,

1 The basic concepts are available in Louis Guttman, "A Basis for Scaling Qualitative Data," *American Sociological Review*, 9:139–50, 1944.

validity, and the like, he is referred to the forthcoming books on the work of the Research Branch.

The Scalogram Analysis Approach. The Cornell technique is a procedure for testing the hypothesis that a universe of qualitative data is a scale for a given population of people, using the scalogram approach. It can also be used to test the hypothesis that the data form a quasi-scale. Of the several techniques now available for scalogram analysis,[2] the one to be described here seems to be among the simplest and most convenient for general use. It requires no special equipment and involves only very simple clerical procedures which can readily be carried out by persons unskilled in statistics.

The various techniques just referred to all do the same job since they follow the same scalogram theory; they differ only in how the work is arranged. The initial steps are common to all. First, the universe of content to be studied is defined. In an attitude or opinion study, this means deciding on the general content of the questions to be asked. Second, the population of people is defined. In an attitude or opinion survey, this means that the class of people to be interviewed is delimited.

Next come two kinds of sampling problems. One kind is the ordinary problem of random sampling of people, and the other is the sampling of items. For these two sampling problems, it is helpful to distinguish between the pre-test stage of a study and the final survey. Much fewer people can be used in a pre-test than must be used in the final survey, but less items can be used in the final survey than must be used in the pretest.

In the pre-test for a survey, about one hundred persons will usually constitute an adequate sample of the population to test the hypothesis of scalability. If the hypothesis is accepted, the items can then be used in the final study of the usual three thousand or so people to obtain reliable proportions at each scale rank.

[2] The first technique employed laborious least squares computations. See Louis Guttman, "The Quantification of a Class of Attributes: A Theory and Method of Scale Construction," in P. Horst et al., *The Prediction of Personal Adjustment,* Social Science Research Council, 1941, pp. 319–48. The standard procedure used by the Research Branch involves the use of scalogram boards especially invented for this purpose by the writer; these boards are simple to build and operate, and a description of them will be in the forthcoming publication. A tabulation technique has been devised by another member of the Research Branch; see Ward H. Goodenough, "A Technique for Scale Analysis," *Educational and Psychological Measurement,* 4:179–90, 1944. The Cornell technique was devised by the writer at first for teaching purposes, and has proved to be very useful for general research purposes. A brief statement of the procedure as carried out on IBM equipment has already been noted in E. William Noland, "Worker Attitude and Industrial Absenteeism: A Statistical Approach," *American Sociological Review,* 10:503–10, 1945.

The other sampling problem is of quite a different nature; it consists of sampling the universe of content. In an attitude or opinion survey, this is done by constructing some questions which contain the required general content. In a pre-test, about a dozen questions usually can constitute an adequate sampling of the content. Since questions are constructed by the research workers, they do not fall into any standard random sampling scheme, and standard random sampling theory does not apply here. Instead, it is shown by the theory of scale analysis that *almost any* sample of about a dozen questions from the universe is adequate to test the hypothesis that the universe is scalable, provided that the range of content desired is covered by the questions. If the hypothesis is accepted that the universe is scalable, then less questions can be used in the final study if fewer ranks are actually needed for the purposes of the final research.

Having defined the universe of content and the population of people, and having drawn a sample from each, the fifth step is to observe each person in the sample on each item or question in the sample. In an attitude or opinion survey where a questionnaire is used, this involves having the people indicate their answers to each question of the questionnaire.

The Hypothesis of Scalability. The problem now is to test the hypothesis, on the basis of the pre-test sample data, that the entire universe of items forms a scale for the entire population of people. Let us review what this hypothesis implies in order to see what the technique of analysis is trying to do.

The universe is said to be scalable for the population if it is possible to rank the people from high to low in such a fashion that from a person's rank alone we can reproduce his response to each of the items in a simple fashion.[3] It is understood that a perfect scale is not to be expected in practice. Data have been considered sufficiently scalable if they are about 90 per cent reproducible, and if certain other conditions (to be explained later) are satisfied. For clarity, though, let us consider first a hypothetically perfect scale.

Suppose that a question from the universe is asked of a population concerning a certain political issue and that the responses are as follows:

Agree	60%
Undecided	10
Disagree	30
	100%

[3] For a basic discussion of the theory of scales, see Louis Guttman, "A Basis for Scaling Qualitative Data," *ibid.*

If "Agree" means a more favorable opinion than "Undecided," if "Undecided" is more favorable than "Disagree," and if the universe is perfectly scalable, then the following must be true. The highest 60 per cent of the people must be those who said "Agree"; the next highest 10 per cent must be those who said "Undecided"; and the lowest 30 per cent must be those who "Disagree." If another question from this scalable universe is asked and the responses are 20 per cent "Yes" and 80 per cent "No," and if "Yes" means a more favorable attitude than "No," then the top 20 per cent of the people must be those who said "Yes" and the bottom 80 per cent must be those who said "No." From the rank of a person, we can now deduce what his response must be to each of these two questions. Any person in the top 20 per cent of the population must have said "Agree" to the first question and "Yes" to the second question. Any person lower than the top 20 per cent but not lower than the top 60 per cent said "Agree" to the first question and "No" to the second question. Any person below the top 60 per cent but not below the top 70 per cent said "Undecided" to the first question and "No" to the second, and the rest of the people, the bottom 30 per cent, said "Disagree" to the first question and "No" to the second.

The various techniques for scalogram analysis are devices to find the rank order for the people which will best reproduce their responses to each of the items in this fashion. If the universe were a perfect scale, all of the techniques would involve little work and there would not be much to choose between them. It is the presence of imperfect reproducibility that raises the problem of technique.

The Cornell technique works by successive approximations. Usually just two approximations suffice to reject or accept the hypothesis of scalability. A first trial rank order for the people is established by a simple scoring scheme. For illustrative purposes, let us work out an actual case in detail. This illustration is not to be taken as a model of perfect research, but rather only to provide an example of the steps to be followed.

An Example of the Cornell Technique. It was desired to find out if the students in a certain class in race relations had a scalable attitude toward one of their textbooks, *A Nation of Nations,* by Louis Adamic. A questionnaire with seven questions was made out and administered to the class of fifty students. Both the number of questions and the number of students are smaller than those ordinarily to be used in a pre-test; they are used here only because these smaller numbers permit displaying the full data.

The seven questions were as follows:

A Nation of Nations

Questions

1. *A Nation of Nations* does a good job of analyzing the ethnic groups in this country.
   _____ Strongly agree$_4$ _____ Agree$_3$ _____ Undecided$_2$ _____ Disagree$_1$ _____ Strongly disagree$_0$

2. On the whole, *A Nation of Nations* is not as good as most college textbooks.
   _____ Strongly agree$_0$ _____ Agree$_1$ _____ Undecided$_2$ _____ Disagree$_3$ _____ Strongly disagree$_4$

3. Adamic organizes and presents his material very well.
   _____ Strongly agree$_4$ _____ Agree$_3$ _____ Undecided$_2$ _____ Disagree$_1$ _____ Strongly disagree$_0$

4. As a sociological treatise, Adamic's book does not rate very high.
   _____ Strongly agree$_0$ _____ Agree$_1$ _____ Undecided$_2$ _____ Disagree$_3$ _____ Strongly disagree$_4$

5. Adamic does not discuss any one group in sufficient detail so that a student can obtain a real insight into problems of ethnic group relations in this country.
   _____ Strongly agree$_0$ _____ Agree$_1$ _____ Undecided$_2$ _____ Disagree$_3$ _____ Strongly disagree$_4$

6. By providing a panorama of various groups, *A Nation of Nations* lets the student get a good perspective on ethnic group relations in this country.
   _____ Strongly agree$_4$ _____ Agree$_3$ _____ Undecided$_2$ _____ Disagree$_1$ _____ Strongly disagree$_0$

7. *A Nation of Nations* is good enough to be kept as a textbook for this course.
   _____ Strongly agree$_4$ _____ Agree$_3$ _____ Undecided$_2$ _____ Disagree$_1$ _____ Strongly disagree$_0$

CONTENT SCALE ANALYSIS

We now describe, step by step, how the analysis of the responses is carried out by the Cornell technique:

1. Weights for the first trial are assigned to each category of each question, using the successive integers beginning with zero. In this example, since each set of answers had five categories, the weights range from 0 to 4. In each question, the higher weights are assigned to the categories judged to express a more favorable attitude. This judging of

ranks of categories is not to be regarded as final; the consequent analysis will either verify the judging or determine how to revise it.

2. A total score is obtained for each person by adding up the weights of the categories he falls into. In our example, since the maximum weight for each person is four, and the total number of questions is seven, the total scores can range from zero to twenty-eight.

3. The questionnaires are shuffled into rank order according to the total scores. In our example, we have arranged them from high to low.

4. A table is prepared, like Table 1, on page 66, with one column for each category of each question and one row for each person. Since each of our questions has five categories, and since there are seven questions, we have thirty-five columns in our table. There are fifty students, so we have fifty rows. The first five columns are for the five categories of the first question, the second five columns for the five categories of the second question, etc.

5. The response of each person to each question is indicated on the table by placing an X in his row in the column for each category into which he falls. In our example, we have labeled the columns according to the questions and the weights of the categories. The first person is the one with the highest score, which is 28. He had checked the response weighted 4 in each of the questions, so he has seven X's in his row, each under the respective columns for the categories with weight 4. There were two persons with a score of 25. The arrangement of people with the same score is arbitrary. Of the two persons in our example with a score of 25, the one placed first had a response of 4 to the first two questions, a response of 3 to the third question, of 4 to the fourth question, of 3 to the fifth and sixth questions, and of 4 to the seventh question. Similarly, the X's in Table 1 indicate the response of each of the remaining persons to each question. Every person answers every question [4] so that there are seven X's in each row. *Table 1 is a complete record of all the data obtained by the survey with respect to this area.*

6. At the bottom of Table 1 are the frequencies of response for each category. Category 4 of question 1 had nine people in it, whereas category 3 of the same question had twenty-seven people, etc. The sum of the frequencies of the five categories in each question is always the total number of people in the sample, which in this case is fifty.

7. Now we come to the test for scalability. If the universe is a scale and if the order in which we have placed the people is the scale rank order, then the pattern of X's in Table 1 must be of a particularly simple

---

[4] If people sometimes fail to respond to a question, then another category is added entitled "No Answer," which is weighted and treated like any other category for that question. In the present example, there were no "No Answers."

TABLE 1
A NATION OF NATIONS
First Trial: Content

Score	1					2					3					4					5					6					7		
	4	3	2	1	0	4	3	2	1	0	4	3	2	1	0	4	3	2	1	0	4	3	2	1	0	4	3	2	1	0	4	3	2
28	x					x					x					x					x					x					x		
25	x					x						x				x						x					x				x		
25	x					x					x							x			x					x					x		
24	x						x				x						x				x					x					x		
23	x						x				x					x						x						x			x		
23	x						x				x							x			x					x					x		
23		x				x						x					x				x						x						x
22	x						x				x							x			x						x				x		
21		x					x					x					x				x						x					x	
21		x					x					x					x				x						x					x	
21	x						x					x					x					x					x					x	
21		x				x						x						x			x						x					x	
21		x				x					x							x						x		x					x		
20		x					x				x						x				x						x						x
20			x			x						x					x				x					x					x		
20	x						x					x					x						x			x					x		
20	x						x				x						x						x				x					x	
19	x						x				x							x			x						x					x	
19	x							x					x				x				x							x			x		
18		x					x					x					x						x				x					x	
18		x					x					x					x							x		x						x	
18		x					x						x				x						x				x					x	
18		x					x						x					x			x						x					x	
17		x					x					x						x				x					x					x	
17		x				x						x						x				x						x				x	
16		x					x						x					x				x					x					x	
16		x						x					x					x			x						x					x	
16		x						x				x				x								x			x					x	
16		x					x					x						x				x					x						x
15		x					x					x						x				x					x						x
15			x					x				x							x		x						x					x	
15		x					x				x						x						x				x						x
14			x				x						x				x					x					x						x
14		x					x				x								x			x						x					x
13			x						x		x								x			x				x							x
13		x							x		x					x						x						x					x
12			x				x							x		x						x						x					x
12	x						x							x		x						x						x					x
11	x							x					x						x			x						x					x
11		x						x					x				x					x						x					x
10			x					x			x								x			x				x							x
9	x								x		x								x		x						x					
8			x					x			x								x		x							x					x
7	x								x		x								x		x					x						
7			x						x		x							x					x				x						x
7			x						x					x			x				x						x						x
6			x						x					x					x		x						x						x
5			x						x					x			x							x			x					
5			x							x			x						x				x				x					
4			x							x	x								x				x						x			
Freq.	9	27	2	12	0	8	24	0	13	5	10	25	8	7	0	3	7	16	14	10	3	14	5	21	7	9	21	7	12	1	11	19	5 1

kind. Let us consider the first question in the Table. If response 4 is higher than response 3, and if 3 is higher than 2, and if 2 is higher than 1 (response 0 happens to have no frequency in this case), then the nine people in category 4 should be the top nine people. Actually, six of them are the top six and the other three scatter farther down the column. Similarly, the twenty-seven people in category 3 should be below the first nine people and should go down to the thirty-sixth person ($36 = 9 + 27$). Again, this is not perfectly true for our data. A similar examination for the other items shows that there is substantial error of reproducibility in their present form. The approximate number of errors need not be counted at this stage, since it is evidently more than 15 per cent of all the 350 responses ($350 = 7 \times 50$, the number of questions times the number of people) in Table 1.

8. It has seldom been found that an item with four or five categories will be sufficiently reproducible if the categories are regarded as distinct. One reason for this is verbal habits of people. Some people may say "Strongly Agree" where others may say "Agree," whereas they have essentially the same position on the basic continuum but differ on an extraneous factor of verbal habits. By combining categories, minor extraneous variables of this kind can be minimized. By examining the overlapping of the X's within the columns of each question, it can be determined how best to combine the categories so as to minimize error of reproducibility for the combinations. In question 2, for example, categories 4 and 3 seem to intertwine, so they are combined. Similarly, in the same question, categories 1 and 0 seem to intertwine, so they are combined. In question 4, on the other hand, we combine categories 3, 2, and 1, leaving categories 4 and 0 separate. The way to combine categories is determined for each question separately. The following are the combinations decided upon for this example on the basis of Table 1:

TABLE 2

COMBINATIONS OF CATEGORIES

Question	Combinations
1	(4) (3) (2, 1, 0)
2	(4, 3) (2, 1, 0)
3	(4, 3, 2) (1, 0)
4	(4) (3, 2, 1) (0)
5	(4, 3, 2) (1, 0)
6	(4, 3) (2, 1, 0)
7	(4) (3) (2, 1, 0)

If it is desired to keep many scale types, then as little combination as possible should be done. However, if not many scale types are desired, the categories may be combined as far as one wishes even though this may not raise reproducibility. There is no harm in combining categories that could otherwise remain distinct with respect to scale error; all that is lost by such a combination is one scale type. On the other hand, categories may *require* combination in order to reduce error; they should be combined in the manner indicated by Table 1 and not arbitrarily.

9. A second trial rank order for the people can now be established on the basis of the combined categories. This is done by reassigning weights. Since the first question now has three categories (that is, three combinations), these are assigned the weights 0, 1, and 2. Question 2 now has two categories. These could be assigned the weights 0 and 1. In the present example, the weights 0 and 2 are used instead, since keeping the rank weights relatively constant from item to item often helps to establish a better ranking for the people when there is error of reproducibility present.[5]

10. Each person is now given a new score which represents his second trial rank order. This is done by rescoring his questionnaire according to the new weights. This rescoring is easily done from Table 1. Using a strip of paper which is as wide as the Table, the new weights for the old categories can be written directly on the edge of the strip. Placing the strip across the row for a person, the weights are added according to where the X's lie. For our example, the strip would have for its first five columns the weights 2, 1, 0, 0, 0, weight 2 being placed in the column which was the old category 4, the weight 1 in the column which was the old category 3, and the 0's being in the old columns 2, 1, and 0 which are now combined. For question 2, the strip would have for the five columns the weights 2, 2, 0, 0, 0. Similarly, the new weights for the other questions can be written down to be used over the old columns of Table 1. The person who was formerly first on Table 1, with a score of 28, now has a score of $2 + 2 + 2 + 2 + 2 + 2 + 2 = 14$. The second person in Table 1 also gets a score of 14. The third person in Table 1 now gets a score of $2 + 2 + 2 + 1 + 2 + 2 + 2 = 13$; and so on for each person.

11. The people are now shifted into the rank order of their new scores, and Table 3 is prepared from the combined data just as Table 1 was prepared from the original data. Question 1 now has three columns, question 2 two columns, etc. The data of Table 1 are modified to fit Table 3 according to the combinations indicated in Table 2. The

[5] In a perfect scale, *any* set of weights, provided they have the proper rank order for the categories, will yield a perfect rank ordering for the people.

TABLE 3
A NATION OF NATIONS
Second Trial: Content

Score	1			2		3		4			5		6		7		
	2	1	0	2	0	2	0	2	1	0	2	0	2	0	2	1	0
14	x			x		x		x			x		x		x		
14	x			x		x		x			x		x		x		
13	x			x		x			x		x		x		x		
13	x			x		x			x		x		x		x		
13	x			x		x			x		x		x		x		
13	x			x		x			x		x		x		x		
12	x			x		x		x			x			x	x		
12	x			x		x			x		x		x			x	
11		x		x		x			x		x		x			x	
11		x		x		x			x		x		x			x	
11		x		x		x			x		x		x			x	
11			x	x		x			x		x		x		x		
11		x		x		x			x		x		x			x	
11		x		x		x			x		x		x			x	
11		x		x		x			x		x		x			x	
11		x		x		x			x		x		x			x	
11		x		x		x			x		x		x			x	
10		x		x		x			x			x	x		x		
10		x		x		x			x		x		x				x
10		x		x		x			x			x	x		x		
9	x				x	x			x		x			x	x		
9		x		x		x			x			x	x			x	
9		x		x		x			x			x	x			x	
9		x		x		x			x			x	x			x	
9		x		x		x			x			x	x			x	
9		x			x	x			x		x		x			x	
8		x		x		x			x			x	x				x
7		x		x		x			x			x		x		x	
7		x			x	x			x			x	x			x	
7			x		x	x				x	x		x			x	
6			x	x			x		x			x	x			x	
6		x		x		x			x			x		x			x
6		x		x		x			x			x		x			x
6		x		x		x			x			x		x			x
6			x		x	x			x			x	x			x	
5			x		x	x			x		x			x			x
4		x			x	x			x			x		x			x
4		x		x			x		x			x		x			x
4			x		x	x				x		x	x				x
3		x			x	x				x		x		x			x
3			x	x			x	x				x		x			x
3		x			x	x				x		x		x			x
2			x		x	x				x		x		x			x
2			x		x	x				x		x		x			x
2			x		x	x				x		x		x			x
2			x		x	x				x		x		x			x
1		x			x		x			x		x		x			x
1			x		x		x		x			x		x			x
1			x		x		x		x			x		x			x
0			x		x		x			x		x		x			x
Freq.	9	27	14	32	18	43	7	3	37	10	22	28	30	20	11	19	20

columns of Table 3 now refer to the combined categories, and the scores of Table 3 are the second trial scores just obtained in the preceding step.

12. The error of reproducibility in Table 3 seems much smaller than in Table 1, and we shall now count up the actual errors. This is done by establishing *cutting points* in the rank order of the people which separate them according to the categories in which they would fall if the scale were perfect. For question 1, which has three categories, we need two cutting points. The first seems to fall between the last person with score 12 and the first person with score 11. All people above this cutting point should be in category 2, and all people below should not be in category 2. Since there is one person in category 2 below this point, we have one error for category 2. A second cutting point is needed to separate category 1 from category 0; since these two categories overlap somewhat, its exact location is not essential since moving it slightly up or down will not change the amount of error. It should be placed so as to minimize the error, but this may be done in several adjacent ways. One way is to place the cutting point between the second and third persons with score 4. Below this point we find three errors in category 1, and above this, we find five errors in category 0. The total number of errors in question 1 is $1 + 3 + 5 = 9$. Since there are fifty responses to question 1, this means 18 per cent error. This error could be reduced, of course, by combining the last two columns and leaving question 1 as a dichotomy. Then there would be only the one error in the first column. Such a further dichotomization need not be done if there is relatively little error in the other questions so that the error over all questions is not much more than 10 per cent.

Question 2 has two categories in the second trial, and the cutting point which will minimize the error is between the last two scores 6, which makes two errors in the first column and four errors in the second column of question 2. Similarly, question 3 has a cutting point between the last score 2 and the first score 1, leaving three errors in its second column. Question 4 gets two cutting points, questions 5 and 6 one cutting point, and question 7 two cutting points. The total number of errors in the whole of Table 3 is 40, which is 11 per cent of all the responses. We can, therefore, conclude in view of the fact that much of the error occurs in question 1 and could be eliminated by combining two categories in that question, that this area is scalable. From a person's rank order, we can reproduce his response to each question *in terms of combined categories* with 89 per cent accuracy (or better, if we combine the last two columns of question 1).

13. The per cent reproducibility alone is not sufficient to lead to the conclusion that the universe of content is scalable. The frequency of

responses to each separate item must also be taken into account for a very simple reason. Reproducibility can be artificially high simply because one category in each item has a very high frequency. It can be proved that the reproducibility of an item can never be less than the largest frequency of its categories, regardless of whether the area is scalable or not. For example, question 3 in Table 3 has quite an extreme kind of distribution. Forty-three students are in one category, and seven in the other. Under no circumstances, then, could there be more than seven errors made on this item, regardless of whether or not a scale pattern existed. Or again, question 4 in Table 3 has thirty-seven cases in its modal category and thirteen cases in the other two categories. Under no circumstances, then, could item 4 have more than thirteen errors. Clearly, the more evenly the frequencies are distributed over the categories of a given item, the harder it is for reproducibility to be spuriously high. Questions 5 and 6 in Table 3 each have high reproducibility, each having five errors; these are not artificially high because question 5 has only twenty-eight cases in its more frequent category, and question 6 has thirty cases for its modal frequency. The maximum possible error for question 5 is twenty-two, and for question 6 it is twenty. The scale pattern represents quite a substantial reduction from this maximum error. An empirical rule for judging the spuriousness of scale reproducibility has been adopted to be the following: no category should have more error in it than non-error. Thus, the category with weight 2 in question 1 (Table 3) has eight non-errors and one error; category with weight 1 in this same question has twenty-four non-errors and three errors; category 0 has nine non-errors and five errors. Thus question 1 fits this rule. Question 3 comes perilously near not fitting the rule. While the first column of question 3 (in Table 3) has no error, the second column has three errors compared to four non-errors. Similarly, the first column of question 4 has one error compared to two non-errors. It is because evenly distributed questions like 5 and 6 have little error and because the errors in the other questions, like in 3 and 4, are not too widely displaced from where they ought to be, that we consider this area to be scalable.

In constructing a sample of items to be used in a test for scalability, at least some of the items should be constructed, if at all possible, to obtain a uniform distribution of frequencies. Such items afford a good test of scalability. However, items with non-uniform frequencies are also needed in order to get differentiated scale types, so both kinds of items must be used. The more categories that are retained in an item, the sharper is the test for scalability, because error—if it really should be there—has a better possibility to appear when there are more categories.

INTENSITY ANALYSIS

Separating "Favorable" from "Unfavorable" People. Since the expression of opinion about the textbook, *A Nation of Nations,* is sufficiently scalable, it is meaningful to say that one student likes the book better than another. There is a meaningful rank ordering of the students according to their opinion of the book. This ordering is expressed by the scale scores assigned in the second trial. A student with a higher score than another says the same or better things about the book (within scale error).

There is a further question that is of interest to the research worker. Given that the individuals can be ranked according to their degree of favorableness, is there a cutting point in this rank order such that we can say that all people to the right of the point are "favorable" and all people to the left are "unfavorable?" One person may be more favorable than another, yet both may be favorable. Obtaining just a rank order does not distinguish between being favorable and being unfavorable; it merely reflects being *more* favorable and *less* favorable and does not tell if a point is reached beyond which being *less* favorable actually means being "unfavorable."

An objective answer to this problem is provided by the use of the *intensity function.*

The theory of intensity analysis will be explained in detail in the forthcoming publication on the work of the Research Branch.[6] For our purposes, all we need to know is that it provides a solution to the traditional problem of question bias. No matter how questions are worded or loaded, use of the intensity function will yield the same proportion of the group as favorable and unfavorable. The intensity function provides an invariant zero point for attitudes and opinions.

There are several techniques for obtaining intensity in a questionnaire, as will be discussed in the volumes to be published on the work of the Research Branch. We shall discuss only two here, as carried out by the Cornell technique. These are very simple indeed to perform. The first is the *fold-over* technique, and the second is the *two-part* technique. The fold-over technique is theoretically less justifiable than the two-part technique. However, it does have some practical advantages in some cases.

The Fold-Over Technique. The fold-over technique consists simply of rescoring the content questions in order to obtain an intensity score. This is easily done for the form of question used to study opinions about

---

[6] See also, Louis Guttman and Edward A. Suchman, "Intensity and a Zero-Point for Attitude Analysis," to appear in the *American Sociological Review.*

A Nation of Nations. The following weights are assigned to the check
list of answers: "Strongly agree" and "Strongly disagree" receive a
weight of 2; "Agree" and "Disagree" receive a weight of 1; and "Undecided" receives a weight of 0.[7] Thus, the apparently more intense
responses receive higher weights, and the apparently less intense responses receive lower weights, regardless of whether the responses appear to be "favorable" or "unfavorable."

Weighting the responses in this way means that in order to obtain
an intensity score, we are in fact combining opposite ends of the check
list, so that there are but three (combined) intensity categories per question. Intensity, as obtained in this fashion, is not in general scalable.
Instead, it forms what is called a quasi-scale. In a quasi-scale there is no
perfect relationship between a person's response to each question and
his score on all the questions; instead, there is a gradient. The higher a
person's score, the more *likely* he is to give a high response to each item,
but there is not the high certainty that exists in the case of a scale. This
can be seen in our example of Adamic's textbook. Arranging the data
into a scalogram according to total intensity score, we obtain the con-
figuration shown in Table 4. Each question now has three categories
which represent the three intensity steps. There is a density gradient of
responses. There are no clear-cut streaks in the category columns, but
instead gradually tapering densities that blend from one category into
the next. Combining categories still will not yield a scalable pattern.

According to the basic theory of intensity analysis, intensity should be
a perfectly scalable variable. The equations of scale analysis show that
there is a second component in every scale of content which is a U- or
J-shaped function of the scale scores. This component has been identified
as the intensity function of the content scale. What we are trying to
do is to obtain this intensity by direct empirical methods. The fact that
our observed intensity is not perfectly scalable shows that it is not the
pure intrinsic intensity we are seeking. No perfect way has yet been
found for obtaining intensity, but satisfactory results are obtainable
even with imperfect intensity techniques. Instead of a perfect intensity
function, we will get one that can have considerable error in its relationship to the content scale scores.

Plotting Intensity Against Content. The empirical intensity function
is obtained by plotting the intensity scores (Table 4) against the content
scores (Table 3) obtained from the previous section from the second
content trial. The scattergram is shown in Table 5. The frequency in

[7] These weights can be written on a strip of paper to be put over Table 1, and thus
they can be added up according to the x's in Table 1 to obtain an intensity score for
each person.

TABLE 4

A NATION OF NATIONS
Intensity

Score	1			2			3			4			5			6			7	
	2	1	0	2	1	0	2	1	0	2	1	0	2	1	0	2	1	0	2	1
14	x			x			x			x			x			x			x	
12		x		x				x		x			x			x			x	
11		x		x			x				x			x		x			x	
11	x			x				x		x				x			x		x	
11	x					x	x				x			x		x			x	
11	x			x			x					x		x		x			x	
10		x		x				x			x			x		x			x	
10	x					x	x					x		x		x			x	
10	x					x	x				x		x				x		x	
9	x					x	x			x					x			x	x	
9		x		x					x	x			x				x			x
9		x			x			x			x		x				x		x	
9		x		x				x			x		x				x			x
9		x			x			x			x			x			x			x
9		x				x		x		x			x				x			x
9		x		x				x		x				x				x	x	
9		x		x				x		x				x				x	x	
8		x				x		x		x				x			x			x
8		x				x		x		x				x			x			x
8		x				x		x			x		x				x			x
8		x				x		x		x				x			x			x
8		x				x		x				x	x			x				x
8		x				x		x				x		x		x			x	
7		x				x		x			x			x			x			x
7	x					x		x			x				x		x			x
7	x					x			x		x		x					x	x	
7		x				x		x			x			x			x			x
7		x		x				x			x			x				x		x
7		x				x		x			x			x			x			x
7		x				x		x			x			x			x			x
7			x			x		x		x				x			x			x
7		x				x		x			x			x			x			x
7		x				x		x			x			x			x			x
7		x		x				x				x		x			x			x
7		x				x		x			x			x			x			x
7		x				x	x					x	x				x			
6		x				x	x					x		x			x			
6		x				x			x		x			x			x			x
6		x				x			x		x			x			x			x
6		x				x	x					x			x		x			x
6		x				x		x				x		x			x			x
6		x				x		x				x		x			x			x
6		x				x		x				x		x			x			x
6		x				x			x		x			x			x			x
6		x				x		x			x			x			x			
6		x				x		x				x		x			x			x
5		x				x			x	x				x				x		
4		x				x			x			x			x		x			x
4		x				x		x				x	x					x		
3			x			x			x			x			x		x			x
Freq.	9	39	2	13	37	0	10	32	8	13	21	16	10	35	5	10	33	7	15	30

74

TABLE 5

A NATION OF NATIONS

Scattergram of Intensity and Content

Intensity	Content (Second Trial)							Total
	0-2	3-5	6-8	9-10	11	12-13	14	
14							*I*	1
13								0
12	1							1
11				1		2	*I*	4
10					1	2		3
9	*4*	1	1		1	1		8
8	2	1	1	2				6
7	1	1	*4*	2	*4*	1		13
6		*I*	3	4	2			10
5		*I*						1
4		1			1			2
3		1						1
Total	8	7	9	9	9	6	2	50

italics in each column of Table 5 corresponds to the position of the median intensity for the respective columns. If the pure intrinsic intensity were being measured by our technique, there would be no scatter about these medians at all, but intensity would be a perfect U- or J-shaped function of the content scores. Despite the presence of error, however, the approximate shape of the true intensity function is clear from the shape of the curve along which the columnar medians lie. The curve descends from the right, or the more favorable content scores, reaches its low point at the next to the last interval to the left (content scores 3–5), and then rises again at the last interval to the left. The content scores 3–5, then, must be the approximate interval which contains the zero-point of the attitude. Students to the left of this interval can be said to have *negative* attitudes and students to the right can be said to have *positive* attitudes toward the textbook. Students in the 3–5 interval cannot be divided into positives and negatives without the aid of more questions which will help differentiate between their ranks more precisely.

On the basis of Table 5 we can conclude, then, that about eight students did not like the textbook, thirty-five students did like the textbook, while seven students were in between. This division of the students into those with favorable and those with unfavorable attitudes does not depend upon the particular way we worded our questions. The same intensity curve, with the same proportion to the right and to the left of the zero-point, would have been obtained if we had used other questions or other wordings, provided only that these other questions were scalable with the present questions. Proof of this invariant property of the intensity function is given in the forthcoming volumes on the Research Branch's work.

Need for Larger Sample of People. An important caution must be sounded here. The example we are working with must be regarded as a highly fortunate one in one sense for the purposes of this exposition. It is rare indeed to find as low error as we have in the intensity function so that the intensity curve and zero-point show out quite clearly on the basis of our small sample of fifty cases. This will be far from the case in general. To perform an intensity analysis safely, when there is substantial error present—which is the usual case—ordinarily from one to three thousand cases are needed to obtain stable medians. To perform the scalogram analysis, it is also safer to use more than fifty cases. A hundred cases is a desirable minimum to use in the pre-test, as well as a dozen or so items instead of seven as we have used in our illustrative example. If the pre-test has established that the universe of items is scalable, the final study should be done on the usual number of cases used in opinion surveys if reliable results with respect to intensity are to be obtained. The hypothesis of scalability can be tested in a pre-test on relatively few people because of its specialized character. However, *proportions* of the population at any given rank or on one side of the zero-point are subject to ordinary sampling error; larger samples of people must be used for reliable results with respect to them.

Drawbacks to the Fold-Over Technique. The fold-over technique for intensity has two theoretical drawbacks to it, as well as some practical ones. First, the intensity scores obtained thereby are not experimentally independent of the content scores because exactly the same answers are used for both the scores. This may give rise to some spuriousness in the relationship between the two. Second, it assumes that "Strongly agree" and "Strongly disagree" are approximately equal in intensity and opposite in direction, and similarly for "Agree" and "Disagree," while it is assumed that "Undecided" approximately straddles the zero-point. These assumptions need not at all be true. In fact, the occasional falsity of these assumptions is one contribution to error in the obtained intensity scores.

If the assumptions were true, life would be much easier for research workers. It would not be necessary to ask a series of questions in order to obtain a zero interval at all, because the "Undecided" category for any question would provide such an interval. But unfortunately it is clear

that in a series of questions on the same issue, the people who are "Un-decided" on one question can all be "Agreed" on another question. It is just because we cannot interpret the bias of a question by looking at its content that such a technique as that of the intensity function is needed.

While the fold-over technique does have these two theoretical draw-backs, it does seem to average out the errors involved in violating the above assumptions and to provide a proper U- or J-shaped curve in many cases.

A practical disadvantage to the fold-over technique has been found in the case of man-in-the-street interviews, where people would avoid the "strongly" categories almost completely, so that not much differen-tiation in intensity could be obtained. In such a case, a two-part tech-nique is necessary. An advantage of the fold-over over the two-part technique is that it takes less space and time in administering question-naires. The two-part technique will be illustrated in the next example.

ANOTHER EXAMPLE OF CONTENT AND INTENSITY ANALYSIS

A Universe Is not Necessarily a Scale. A set of items constructed from a single universe of content is not necessarily scalable. The notion of universe of content and the notion of scalability are quite distinct. If a universe of content is not scalable, it can sometimes be broken down into sub-universes, some of which may be scalable separately. If a uni-verse is not scalable for a given population of people, then it is not meaningful to assign a single rank order to the people with respect to the total content. Indeed, if arbitrary scores were assigned to non-scalable data, intensity analysis should find that there was no U- or J-shaped intensity function and no invariant zero-point for dividing the population into positives and negatives.

An example of such a non-scalable case is the one next to be given. It will also illustrate the two-part intensity technique. The content for this second example concerns another textbook used in the same course as the first. The fifty students in the class were asked the following ques-tions about *Black Metropolis* (by Drake and Cayton).

BLACK METROPOLIS

Questions

1. (a) On the whole, as textbooks go, how good do you think *Black Metropolis* is? (Check one answer)

_____ Very good$_5$ _____ Good$_4$ _____ Fairly Good$_3$
_____ Passable$_2$ _____ Not very good$_1$ _____ Terrible$_0$

(b) How strongly do you feel about this? (Check one answer)
_____ Very strongly$_3$ _____ Pretty strongly$_2$ _____ Somewhat strongly$_1$ _____ Not strongly at all$_0$

2. (a) In your opinion, does *Black Metropolis* present a good socio-logical analysis of the Negro community in Chicago?
_____ An excellent analysis$_5$ _____ A very good analysis$_4$
_____ A pretty good analysis$_3$ _____ It has only a few good points$_2$
_____ Not a very good analysis$_1$ _____ A pretty bad analysis$_0$

(b) How strongly do you feel about this?
_____ Very strongly$_3$ _____ Pretty strongly$_2$ _____ Somewhat strongly$_1$ _____ Not strongly at all$_0$

3. (a) To what extent does the book afford the student a real insight into the problems of race relations in Chicago?
_____ Not much at all$_0$ _____ A somewhat limited insight$_1$
_____ Fairly good insight$_2$ _____ A good insight$_3$ _____ A very good insight$_4$ _____ An excellent insight$_5$

(b) How strongly do you feel about this?
_____ Very strongly$_3$ _____ Pretty strongly$_2$ _____ Somewhat strongly$_1$ _____ Not strongly at all$_0$

4. (a) In general, how well does the book organize and present its material?
_____ Very poorly$_0$ _____ Not very well$_1$ _____ Fairly well$_2$
_____ Quite well$_3$ _____ Very well$_4$

(b) How strongly do you feel about this?
_____ Very strongly$_3$ _____ Pretty strongly$_2$ _____ Somewhat strongly$_1$ _____ Not strongly at all$_0$

5. (a) Some parts of *Black Metropolis* emphasize statistical data and other parts quote personal interviews a great deal. Do you believe that the authors have succeeded in blending these data properly, or have they failed?
_____ Succeeded very well$_4$ _____ Succeeded pretty well$_3$
_____ Succeeded at least more than they have failed$_2$ _____ Pretty much failed$_1$ _____ Definitely failed$_0$

(b) How strongly do you feel about this?
_____ Very strongly$_3$ _____ Pretty strongly$_2$ _____ Somewhat strongly$_1$ _____ Not strongly at all$_0$

6. (a) Some students complain that the textbook often makes fuzzy statements, so that it is not clear what position it takes or what it is driving at. To what extent do you agree with this complaint?
_____ Completely agree$_0$ _____ Agree for the most part$_1$
_____ Undecided$_2$ _____ Disagree$_3$ _____ Completely disagree$_4$

(b) How strongly do you feel about this?

_____ Very strongly$_3$ _____ Pretty strongly$_2$ _____ Somewhat strongly$_1$ _____ Not strongly at all$_0$

7. (a) Do you think *Black Metropolis* is good enough to be kept as a textbook for this course?

_____ Definitely yes$_4$ _____ Yes$_3$ _____ Undecided$_2$ _____ No$_1$ _____ Definitely not$_0$

(b) How strongly do you feel about this?

_____ Very strongly$_3$ _____ Pretty strongly$_2$ _____ Somewhat strongly$_1$ _____ Not strongly at all$_0$

Each question is in two parts. The first part is to study content, and the second part is to study intensity. Notice that the number of categories in the content parts is not uniform from question to question. It is not essential for a scalogram analysis that there be any uniform format for the questions. In the same series of items, some can be trichotomies, some can have six categories, and some can have two categories, etc., etc. Nor is the wording of the categories of special importance. Short phrases or long phrases, etc., can be used. Five and six categories were used in the present example because it was suspected in advance that the students would give apparently favorable answers to all questions put to them, so the apparently favorable responses were made more numerous in the check list of answers in order to help obtain differentiation in rankings.

The Cornell technique was used to analyze the content parts of the seven questions on *Black Metropolis*. The first trial weights are those indicated with the questions, and the first trial scalogram is shown in Table 6. All the items were found to have so much error that they required dichotomization. The combinations of categories used and the results of the second trial are shown in Table 7. There is still too much error in Table 7. Several of the questions have more error than nonerror. We therefore judge the total content not to be scalable, since no further trials can be made when all items are dichotomous.

Therefore we cannot speak of degrees of "favorableness" of opinion about *Black Metropolis* for this class of students. We cannot say that one student likes the book better than another student. He may like it better in one of the aspects and not better in another. There is apparently not a single ranking possible in the total content studied by the questionnaire. If the study were to be carried further, what would be done to try to break the content down into sub-areas, make up a dozen or so questions for each of the sub-areas, administer the sub-areas to the

TABLE 6
BLACK METROPOLIS
First Trial: Content

Column groups (each with sub-scores): **1** (5 4 3 2 1 0) · **2** (5 4 3 2 1 0) · **3** (5 4 3 2 1 0) · **4** (4 3 2 1 0) · **5** (4 3 2 1 0) · **6** (4 3 2 1 0) · **7** (4 3 2 …)

Score	1-5	1-4	1-3	1-2	1-1	1-0	2-5	2-4	2-3	2-2	2-1	2-0	3-5	3-4	3-3	3-2	3-1	3-0	4-4	4-3	4-2	4-1	4-0	5-4	5-3	5-2	5-1	5-0	6-4	6-3	6-2	6-1	6-0	7-4	7-3	7-2
30	x						x						x						x					x						x				x		
29		x					x						x							x				x					x					x		
28	x						x						x							x					x					x				x		
28	x								x					x					x					x						x				x		
28	x									x			x						x					x						x				x		
27		x								x			x							x				x					x					x		
27	x						x							x						x				x							x			x		
27	x							x					x						x						x				x							x
27	x							x						x					x						x				x					x		
26		x					x							x					x						x					x				x		
26	x						x							x						x				x						x				x		
26	x						x							x					x					x								x		x		
26		x					x							x						x				x						x				x		
26		x					x							x					x					x						x						x
26	x						x							x					x						x					x				x		
25	x									x						x			x						x					x				x		
25		x						x					x							x					x					x				x		
25	x							x					x								x				x						x			x		
25	x						x						x												x					x			x			
25	x						x						x						x						x					x			x			
24		x								x			x						x						x					x			x			
24		x					x						x								x				x					x			x			
24		x								x			x						x						x					x			x			
24		x						x					x						x						x					x					x	
24			x				x						x						x						x					x				x		
24	x								x				x						x						x						x			x		
23		x						x					x						x						x							x		x		
23		x					x						x						x						x							x			x	
23	x							x								x				x						x			x						x	
23		x						x								x			x						x				x					x		
23	x							x								x			x						x							x	x			
22		x								x					x				x					x								x			x	
22			x					x					x						x					x								x				
22		x						x							x				x						x				x					x		
22	x							x								x				x				x								x	x			
21			x				x								x							x		x								x	x			
21		x					x						x						x							x							x	x		
21		x								x					x				x					x					x					x		
21		x						x							x				x					x							x		x			
20			x							x					x				x					x							x					x
20			x					x								x				x				x					x				x			
19			x							x			x									x		x							x		x			
19			x				x									x			x					x							x		x			
19		x								x			x									x		x								x	x		
18			x				x										x		x					x							x					x
16				x			x							x						x						x			x				x		
16				x					x						x					x							x	x								x
14					x		x						x										x				x	x					x		
14			x					x								x				x					x							x	x		
13			x					x										x		x					x							x	x		
Freq.	18	19	10	2	1	0	12	26	12	0	0	0	12	22	10	4	2	0	14	21	9	5	1	16	26	6	2	0	2	19	12	15	2	20	22	6

TABLE 7
BLACK METROPOLIS
Second Trial: Content

Score	1		2		3		4		5		6		7	
	1	0	1	0	1	0	1	0	1	0	1	0	1	0
7	x		x		x		x		x		x		x	
7	x		x		x		x		x		x		x	
7	x		x		x		x		x		x		x	
7	x		x		x		x		x		x		x	
7	x		x		x		x		x		x		x	
7	x		x		x		x		x		x		x	
7	x		x		x		x		x		x		x	
7	x		x		x		x		x		x		x	
7	x		x		x		x		x		x		x	
7	x		x		x		x		x		x		x	
7	x		x		x		x		x		x		x	
7	x		x		x		x		x		x		x	
7	x		x		x		x		x		x		x	
7	x		x		x		x		x		x		x	
6	x		x		x		x				x		x	
6		x	x		x		x		x		x		x	
6	x			x	x		x		x		x		x	
6	x			x	x		x		x		x		x	
6	x			x	x		x		x		x		x	
6	x		x		x		x		x			x	x	
6	x		x		x		x		x		x		x	
6	x		x		x			x	x		x		x	
6	x			x	x		x		x		x		x	
6	x		x		x			x	x		x		x	
6	x		x		x		x		x			x	x	
6	x		x		x		x		x			x	x	
6	x		x		x		x		x		x		x	
5	x		x			x	x		x		x		x	
5	x		x			x	x		x		x		x	
5	x			x		x	x		x		x		x	
5	x		x			x	x			x	x		x	
5	x		x			x	x		x			x	x	
5	x			x	x		x		x			x	x	
5	x		x		x			x	x			x	x	
5	x		x		x			x	x			x	x	
4		x	x		x		x		x			x		x
4		x	x		x			x	x			x	x	
4		x	x			x		x	x		x		x	
4	x		x			x		x	x			x	x	
4	x			x		x		x	x		x		x	
4	x		x			x		x	x			x	x	
3		x		x	x			x	x			x	x	
3		x	x			x		x	x			x	x	
3		x	x			x	x		x			x		x
3		x		x		x	x		x		x			x
3		x	x		x			x		x	x			x
2		x	x		x			x		x		x		x
1		x		x		x		x		x	x			x
0		x		x		x		x		x		x		x
0		x		x		x		x		x		x		x
Combination	(5, 4) (3, 2, 1, 0)		(5, 4) (3, 2, 1, 0)		(5, 4) (3, 2, 1, 0)		(4, 3) (2, 1, 0)		(4, 3) (2, 1, 0)		(4, 3, 2) (1, 0)		(4, 3) (2, 1, 0)	
Freq.	37	13	38	12	34	16	35	15	42	8	33	17	42	8

TABLE 8
BLACK METROPOLIS
Intensity

	1				2				3				4				5				6				7		
Score	3	2	1	0	3	2	1	0	3	2	1	0	3	2	1	0	3	2	1	0	3	2	1	0	3	2	1
21	x				x				x				x				x				x				x		
20		x			x				x				x				x				x				x		
20		x			x				x				x				x				x				x		
20	x				x				x				x				x					x			x		
19	x				x				x					x			x					x			x		
18	x				x				x					x				x				x			x		
18		x				x			x				x				x					x			x		
18	x				x					x			x				x						x		x		
17		x			x				x					x				x			x						x
17	x				x				x				x				x					x					x
17		x			x					x			x					x			x						x
17	x					x			x				x					x			x						x
17		x			x					x				x			x					x			x		
16		x					x		x						x			x				x			x		
16		x					x			x			x				x					x			x		
16	x				x					x			x				x					x					x
16	x				x				x				x				x						x		x		
16		x			x					x			x				x				x				x		
15		x			x					x			x				x				x						x
15			x		x				x				x				x				x						x
15		x			x				x				x				x							x			x
15		x			x				x				x				x						x				x
15		x					x		x				x				x				x				x		
15			x		x				x				x				x				x						x
14		x				x				x			x				x				x							
14		x					x			x			x				x				x							
14		x			x				x				x				x						x				x
14		x			x					x			x				x						x				x
14		x			x					x					x		x					x			x		
13			x		x					x				x			x					x					x
13		x			x					x				x					x				x		x		
13		x			x					x				x			x					x					x
13		x				x				x					x		x					x					x
13		x				x				x			x				x					x					x
13		x				x				x			x				x					x					x
12		x				x			x						x				x			x						
12			x				x			x				x			x					x			x		
12		x				x				x			x				x					x						
11		x			x					x					x		x							x	x		
11			x		x					x			x				x							x			x
11		x			x					x				x					x					x			x
11		x			x						x			x					x			x					x
11		x			x						x				x		x					x					x
11			x		x						x		x						x		x						
10			x					x			x			x			x				x						
10	x				x				x					x			x					x					
10	x							x			x		x				x				x						
9			x				x			x					x		x				x						x
3				x				x			x					x	x						x				
0				x				x				x				x				x				x			
Freq.	9	31	8	2	20	23	3	4	19	23	7	1	13	25	10	2	15	25	9	1	10	18	16	6	17	21	

class, and analyze each separately by scalogram analysis. Such a further study was not made for this present example.

The Two-Part Intensity Technique. Since the total content is not scalable, it of course should not make much sense to study intensity. However, in order to see how the two-part technique operates, let us go through with it anyhow. Each part (b) of the seven questions on *Black Metropolis* was weighted according to the weights indicated in the list of questions above, and trial intensity scores were obtained thereby. Intensity again seems to be a quasi-scale. Obtaining a quasi-scale, however, has no bearing on the scalability of the *content*. The scalogram for the trial intensity is shown in Table 8. Plotting the trial intensity scores against the second trial content scores yields the scattergram in Table 9. Again, the frequencies in italics in each column indicate the median position for intensity for the respective columns.

TABLE 9

BLACK METROPOLIS

Scattergram of Intensity and Content

Intensity	Content (Second Trial)								Total
	0	1	2	3	4	5	6	7	
21							1		1
20							1	2	3
19						1			1
18					1		1	1	3
17					2	1	1	1	5
16							1	*4*	5
15				1	2		1	2	6
14	1			1		*1*	*1*	1	5
13				*1*		2	*1*	2	6
12		1	1				1		3
11				1	1	1	2	1	6
10				1			2		3
9	1								1
3							1		1
0								1	1
Total	2	1	1	5	6	6	14	15	50

As was warned earlier, fifty cases is far from sufficient to obtain stable column medians when there is substantial intensity error present, which seems to be the case here. However, we have strong reason to believe that the absence of a U- or J-shaped curve of medians in Table 9 is not merely due to sampling error, but rather to the fundamental lack of scalability of the content.

An Intensity Curve from a Final Survey. To give the reader a picture of what final results will look like in practice in a complete study, we present some data from a study by the Research Branch. Ten questions were asked of a cross-section of eighteen hundred enlisted men with respect to expression of job satisfaction in the Army. The content was found to be scalable. Intensity was obtained by the two-part technique. The relationship between intensity and content is shown in Table 10.

TABLE 10

AN EXAMPLE OF THE INTENSITY FUNCTION:

Job Satisfaction in the Army

Intensity Score	Content Score											Total
	0	1	2	3	4	5	6	7	8	9	10	
8	*23*	46	27	33	22	19	24	42	25	23	*24*	308
7	7	*24*	31	26	33	31	22	40	21	*15*	5	255
6	1	7	29	17	30	24	35	42	*15*	11	—	211
5	6	14	14	*29*	20	34	27	*34*	19	10	—	197
4	*2*	3	15	17	*32*	33	*36*	*36*	10	1	—	185
3	—	1	17	19	22	29	33	25	11	1	—	158
2	1	4	9	19	*25*	34	31	32	1	4	1	161
1	—	2	2	12	35	39	38	30	8	—	1	167
0	—	3	7	12	29	43	33	26	3	1	—	157
Total	40	104	151	184	248	286	279	307	103	66	31	1,799

The frequencies in italics in the columns show the median intensity for the respective columns. Content score 5 seems to be approximately the zero interval. Men to the right of this score can be said to have *positive* job satisfaction, and men to the left to have *negative* job satisfaction.

In conclusion, it should be pointed out that the intensity curve provides not only an objective zero point, but also a picture of the relative strength with which an attitude or opinion is held. Differing shaped curves, when plotted on the percentile metric, show differing degrees of sharpness in the division of attitudes or opinions. Illustrations of this will be given in future publications.

THE MEANING OF CONSUMER INTEREST

By
COLSTON E. WARNE
President, Consumers' Union

I

LEST there be misunderstanding, let it be indicated at the outset that the writer is one of that species designated by those in advertising circles as the "professional consumer." For the last decade he has been associated with the growing consumer movement and especially with a testing organization which has now considerably more than a hundred thousand members. We of Consumers Union have been deeply interested in the many local consumer groups which have arisen in all major cities, groups which have been devoting their major attention in recent months to the rescue of the OPA from business lobbies which seek its early destruction. We have likewise been interested in the expanding consumer education movement which promises to make consumers more intelligent and more articulate in years to come. In brief, we are, from the standpoint of many business interests, rebels who feel that our economic system, as at present organized, is not satisfactorily serving the consumer interest. We want changes—rather basic changes. Our view is, we believe, shared by an ever-growing body of citizens whose voice is increasingly being heard. We greatly appreciate the opportunity to present, under these auspices, a viewpoint which to some will not be altogether palatable. Only through a full and free discussion can improved social policies be formulated. We congratulate the University of Pennsylvania for bringing together the diverse groups which have met in this conference.

II

The consumer movement of America has been skeptical of the merit of many business measurements of the consumer, his likes and dislikes. Too often these seem but wasteful devices for extending the sphere of product differentiation. We are skeptical of much of advertising, and hence do not look with favor upon its many satellite measurement agencies as particularly conducive to consumer welfare. We are critical of the quality standards established by business and of its trends in pricing policies, which appear too often tinged with monopoly. We are skeptical of the existing margins in the distributive system which appear often excessive.

Indeed, the business measurements of consumer interests often put us in mind of discussions of fishermen concerning the relative effectiveness of differing types of bait; of the size and species of fish which respond to each type of bait; of the spots within each pool in which hungry fish are likely to congregate. Altogether too often, consumers have in the past been considered legitimate prey. Highly elaborate rules have been established to determine fair fishing practices. The concern has been primarily the gain of the fishermen, and too little attention has been paid to the reaction of the fish to the exploits.

Up to the present, consumer choice has been primarily dictated by business. The arrangement has been justified by its advocates through the optimistic belief that somehow truth and social welfare would emerge triumphant from the exposure of the consumer to competing propagandas financed by partisan advertising interests. The consumer pattern of our society had little serious interference from public education, from the government, or from consumers themselves.

Fortunately this situation is today challenged from a number of sources. Educators are demanding that the schools give impartial guidance—that they supply a new type of consumer education which will appraise competing claims and expose the many frauds with which consumers are surrounded. Many courses have been developed in consumer education both at the high school and at the college level. In most urban centers, consumer groups have been formed. Consumer groups appear at legislative hearings on bills pertaining to housing, medicine, price control, and fair trade practices. In recent months these consumer interest groups have formed the National Emergency Committee for Price Control and have participated actively in the counsels of OPA. Women's clubs have extended their programs to include consumer protection. Government agencies have recognized and to some extent have promoted the growth of the movement. Consumer testing organizations have passed their embryonic stage. In recent months the stage of consumer federation has been reached.

The concept of the consumer organization as an institution within our economic system is relatively new. Yet, with all the efforts which are in action today, there is every reason to forecast that the consumer movement will, like the labor movement, acquire status as a powerful force. At the base will be local consumer councils, including coöperatives, "cost of living committees," women's groups, and educators. These local groups will interest themselves in such problems as housing, retail practices, and collective buying. Local groups will form state federations which will exercise political pressure upon state legislatures in the consumer interest. They will wish a voice in state milk control, in public utility rates, and trade practices laws. On the national level, there is every probability that the groups which have united for price control will form a permanent federation which will be the watch dog of the organized consumers in the national scene.

III

It is perhaps too early to formulate the objectives of the consumer movement. No movement can write its full program in advance. Yet from the evidence it appears that organized consumers are groping toward a program which will include the following major points:

1. Consumers want an impartial check on the quality of the goods they buy. They want to know in understandable terms what service a product will render. Since they have been so often misled by partisan advertising, they will trust as aids to their judgment those agencies— governmental, professional, or consumer-controlled—which have no profit interest in selling them goods.

2. Consumers want legislation which will eliminate worthless or injurious merchandise from the market and will eradicate false and misleading advertising. They want grade labeling of goods and adequate government control of quality standards. They also wish legislative action to minimize high-pressure competitive advertising which, though it may be short of misleading, spoils radio enjoyment, reading pleasure, or scenic beauty without contributing to consumer knowledge.

3. Consumers want a bounty of goods, closely related to our technical potentialities. They have reason to raise an outcry against the restrictive practices of producing groups such as we witnessed throughout the Thirties. They resent the attitude of the believers in free enterprise who hold that it is a sacred right of an owner to close a factory if, at the price set, profits are not satisfactory. They hold that consumers should have a voice in price and output fixation and that our present business management must be deemed incompetent if output is not maximized. Consumers feel that the war experience amply demonstrates their contention that there was no excuse for a pre-war $1,200 median consumption level in a country fully capable, from a production standpoint, of

doubling or trebling that amount. In a word, they wish the economic system not to deliver vague promises but to perform.

4. Consumers wish our educational system to educate for intelligent living in the twentieth century. This must involve guidance in the selection of channels of expenditure and a knowledge of essential facts with respect to commodities. It must involve a realization that courses in buymanship are more significant than courses in salesmanship. This educational program must find its way into adult groups.[1]

Consumer interests have, as a result of the war economy, departed somewhat from this list of broad objectives. Quite naturally, the central focus has in recent years been on price control. No other group has been so ardent in championing the doctrines of Chester Bowles and Paul Porter. To the consumer movement the OPA represented the one means by which, in a period of short supply, inflationary trends might be held in check. The consumer criticism has been, not that the OPA has been too severe in its pricing standards, but that it has consistently been too lax. Consumers have watched the mounting profit levels of business and have felt that OPA was consistently too loose in administration, too tardy in introducing rationing, and too anxious to decontrol products. To be sure, consumer groups have been well aware of the handicaps under which OPA has operated—the division of authority, the amendments introduced by special interests to protect their position, and the enormous enforcement problem. Yet, with the menace of inflation so apparent, it has been difficult for organized consumers to understand the viewpoint of the National Association of Manufacturers and allied groups which have sought to eradicate all price control and allow our economic system to enter a period of uncontrolled inflation.

That the Congress has to date failed to vote in accordance with the consumer viewpoint has convinced consumers that there is a need for redressing the balance between the strong lobbies of organized producer groups and that of consumers. We cannot have effective price control if exceptions are to be made for cotton growers, textile manufacturers, auto dealers, farmers, oil companies, and other interests. And if effective price controls are prematurely abandoned, we are likely to face a wave of strikes which will extend beyond anything within our past experience. In such a race of wages and prices, no economic group can be the permanent victor.

Without question, the interest of consumers in price control has been the most spectacular organizing force in recent years. It has brought delegations to Washington. It has brought consumer picket lines in

[1] This program is adapted from my summary in *Consumer Education, Background, Present Status, and Future Possibilities,* edited by James E. Mendenhall and Henry Harap, D. Appleton-Century, New York, 1943, pp. 10–11.

front of stores. It has been the subject of heated radio debates and mass meetings. It has done more to rally buyers to collective action than any event in our history. Because many members of organized labor have come to recognize that, in a period of controlled wages, the buying power of the dollar is of cardinal importance, this fight has brought marked unity between organized labor and organized consumers. Yet it is highly probable that we are only at the beginning of consumer anti-inflation campaigns. Our monetary supply has so increased, due to war financing through commercial banks, that it will undoubtedly create an upward pressure on prices for years to come. Moreover, with the slackening or abandonment of OPA controls, price increases will result which will give further impetus to consumer agitation.

As time passes, the direction of this agitation will undoubtedly alter. For many years, the bulk of the prices of manufactured commodities have been "price-fixed" by manufacturers. Monopoly and imperfect competition have been so prevalent in our economy that consumers will have cause to inquire whether rising prices may not have been occasioned by organized producer groups. Agitation for price control may speedily give way to agitation against monopolistic practices.

In coming months, we shall undoubtedly witness the widespread use of the weapon of the consumer strike which will grow in force and effectiveness as a means of compelling the squaring of business practices with consumer welfare. Moreover, increasing pressure will be placed upon Congress to enact a program of compulsory grade labeling for canned fruit and vegetables. Consumers will likewise press for extending the work of the National Bureau of Standards to include a wide range of consumer products and the opening of their findings to the public. Not only will consumers urge the development of standards for consumer products; they will also wish the emergence of standardized nomenclature for grades, so that they are no longer faced with a bewildering variety of terms describing the ranking of an article. The experience of the war period, in which the Taft amendment proved an important obstacle in preventing the imposition of quality standards by OPA, has been sufficient to convince consumers of the ease with which producers may lower quality in order to augment profits. Unquestionably the question of grade labeling will be one of the prime points of controversy between organized business and organized consumers.

IV

No discussion of the consumer interest would be complete without reference to the consumer case for reforms in advertising. It is here that consumers feel a particular grievance. The pattern of our civilization has tended increasingly to reflect the desires of those charged with this two-billion-dollar institution. Through the varied channels of the radio, the billboards, and the press, competitive claims for attention beat in upon the buyer. Superficially, the consumer is held to have free choice between ten thousand brands of wheat flour, forty-five hundred brands of canned corn, and five hundred brands of mustard. Superficially, sellers on bended knee appeal for patronage. Yet how much free choice actually prevails when the sellers have studied the whims, caprices, and fears of the consumer and are able to take advantage of the consumer's technical ignorance to make a wise choice remote? Our world has become one of artificial and superficial differentiations, of fraudulent appeals to loyalty. Especially on the radio, convincing commercial appeals are voiced for thousands of articles by voices breathing sincerity and arousing the whole gamut of human emotions.

The drive is one-sided and deceitful. Non-commercial values cannot command the machinery or the money to counsel the consumer to buy the products which possess the best in use values. Everywhere miraculous attributes are associated with even the most staple products. The long-persisting desire of many for ornamentation and differentiation are played upon, until choice becomes no longer free. Style must follow style in endless procession. Goods must be sold, even if this involves rendering useful articles obsolete. The end of production is not that of rendering satisfaction. The consumer exists only to fill the sales quota of industry.

The indictment of advertising is, however, not alone that of its failure to be truthful and to balance values so that the consumer can find his own way amid the conflicting claims. It is also based upon the manner in which the press has become the paid agent of business interests rather than the free instrument for disseminating news and opinion. It is not accidental that the press has generally opposed price control, grade labeling, and other consumer programs. Nor is it accidental that the radio networks have been more generous in their allotment of time to the Fulton Lewises than to the voice of consumers. The media of communication have become instrumentalities of business. They are not free.

V

In the years ahead, the consumer movement will have an important, if difficult, task to perform. It will have to meet the attacks of those who hold it a radical departure from the past. It will have to press for legislative reforms which are opposed by major business interests. It will have to draw together in each community those who have had no tradition of collective action.

Yet the prospects that consumer interests will be recognized have never been brighter. Most important, the American public has witnessed the miracle of war production and has observed that, with our present technical potentialities, poor housing standards, poor nutritional standards, and poor medical standards are unnecessary. Moreover, the thousands of consumers who have worked on price control boards and in anti-inflation campaigns will not quickly sink into inactivity. With the level of consumer education rapidly increasing, the prospects are that powerful consumer organizations will emerge which will prove a needed offset to the restrictive practices of business. The consumer will become a political force whose voice will be respected in Congressional hearings. Business itself will come to recognize that there is a need for "professional consumers" to keep our economic system in balance.

THE MEANING OF MEASUREMENT

PARTICIPANTS

CHAIRMAN: John S. Adams, Jr., *Department of Philosophy, University of Pennsylvania.* SPEAKERS: Edgar A. Singer, Jr., *Department of Philosophy, University of Pennsylvania;* W. Edwards Deming, *Bureau of the Budget;* C. West Churchman, *Department of Philosophy, University of Pennsylvania*

ISOLATION OR COÖPERATION?
By
EDGAR A. SINGER, JR.

THAT professional philosophers should have been active in organizing this and a previous symposium, marked by the participation in them of special scientists; that another philosopher should have found in the contributions of these scientists matters of peculiar interest to himself, not just as a man with personal curiosities, but as a philosopher; that this same philosopher should now find himself addressing his remarks not only to his colleagues but to specialists of whose problems he has no special knowledge—all these circumstances are of pattern so far from traditional as to invite comment, one imagines, in conservative circles. For everything goes to show that in our day most of those who call themselves philosophers, and most of those who call themselves scientists, have come to the conclusion that neither has anything to say to, or learn from, the other. How this sense of mutual aloofness has gradually developed in both camps—for its development has been gradual—is too long a story to review here; but whatever the reasons that brought it about, is there any good reason why it should continue? Is there any profit to either philosopher or scientist in each having as little as possible to do with the other? That is the question on which this paper would offer what few reflections there is time for.

If, as we suppose, the isolationist attitude is more common than the coöperationist, both among philosophers and among scientists, one would expect to find it making the stronger appeal to the respect we all feel for the conservative, the traditional. And, if to make the more obvious is to make the stronger appeal, then we may accord the isolationist attitude this advantage. But it would be a mistake to suppose the coöperationist to be a modern innovator, a wayward wanderer from a respectable past. On the contrary, he would present his case, on historical grounds, as more conservative than that of his isolationist colleague.

But how, one asks, can two reviewers of the same history conceive themselves to be equally conservative of traditional meanings, yet hold such opposite views as to what those meanings are?

It is, I think, because the one view defines the continuities it would preserve, in terms of denotation; the other, in terms of connotation: the one, in terms of problems to be discussed, in whatever way discussed; the other, in terms of the way problems are to be discussed, whatever the problems.

Thus the isolationist philosopher would point out that no important philosophy of the past had failed to address itself to at least some of the topics familiar under the classic captions, *the true, the good, the beautiful;* or again, in later setting, under the headings, *God, freedom, immortality.* Your self-isolating scientist, on the other hand, would conceive his fellows of the past to have been consistently engaged in one or the other of two types of undertaking, mutually dependent for their successful outcome. The one, set down by Galileo at the very beginning of experimental science: "To measure all things measurable and to make measurable all things not [yet] measurable." The other, illustrated at every moment of subsequent progress: to adjust the facts established by measurement to a formal pattern subject to the minimal number of laws.

Now when your philosopher and your scientist respectively conceive themselves dedicated to tasks thus denotatively enumerated, it does seem that nothing either might contribute to the solution of his own, could be of the slightest help toward solving the other man's problems. And yet, if we look a little deeper into the conditions to be met, if progress is to be made toward the solution of either man's problems, we find one such condition common to either man's success. It is the recognition of their common concern with meeting this condition that makes for the coöperative attitude of philosopher and scientist, each toward the other.

What is this condition? Consider for a moment the history of things. The earliest Greek thinkers, Milesian, Ephesian, Eleatic, offered opinions on man, nature, and God that they certainly held to be true, but on what evidence they held them so is in some cases so obscure as to baffle the most studious modern conjecture. But from the time of Socrates (the Platonic Socrates) on, the picture changes; the philosopher proper becomes more and more absorbed in finding out how we are to know whether or not a given opinion is true, less and less concerned with spreading forth an array of opinions that he takes to be so. As reflection develops, the distinction between the problem of method and the gathering of results arrived at by some accepted method grows sharper and more sustained. Consequently your historian of modern philosophy will so classify his characters as to bring into the same school those who most resemble each other in their test of truth, however they may differ in the truths they ultimately believe themselves to have established. Thus if one would know whether a given thinker lies closest to a seventeenth-century Rationalist, an eighteenth-century Empiricist, a late eighteenth- and early nineteenth-century Critical Idealist, or, what I should call, a twentieth-century Experimentalist, it is more significant to learn why he would or would not hold it true that twice two is four, or that there is a sun in the sky, than whether he does or does not believe there to be a God in heaven or good will on earth. For those who give like answers to the first two questions are more likely than those who give like answers to the second pair to hold the same view as to what is and what is not valid in the way of evidence.

Now one who had made his own the historian's understanding of the historic and also permanent meaning of philosophy could hardly be said to have wandered farther from tradition than one who formed his notion of the subject by recalling the more persistent topics on which philosophers had tried out their several theories of evidence. The tenacity with which philosophers throughout the centuries have clung to the same test-questions is to be explained in terms of the superior human interest attaching to the answers arrived at, rather than in terms of any more critical test-value attaching to the questions asked.

But one who accepts at the hands of history the connotative, rather than the denotative definition of philosophy, must accept along with it all the other lessons that this same history imparts; and among these he finds nothing to encourage, but much to discourage, the isolationist point of view. To search the pages of history for all they have to show making for or against this opinion would take a volume. A few sentences suffice to show the kind of record that, if found in these pages, would confirm the coöperationist interpretation of their import. An illustration or two will show that facts of this kind are sometimes found; whether or not they are always in evidence must be left to the judgment of others.

Consider, if you will, the pattern set by the rise, spread, and fall of the first of our modern schools, seventeenth-century Rationalism. The sixteenth century closed in utter confusion of thought concerning all things: a confusion from the midst of which we hear the complaining voice of Montaigne, asking himself, "What goodness is that, which but yesterday I saw in credit and esteem, and tomorrow, to have lost all reputation, and that the crossing of a river, is made a crime? What truth is that, which these mountains bound, and is a lie in the world beyond them?" (II, xii) He cannot, he says, have his judgment so flexible. The seventeenth century opened with the heroic attempt of Descartes to end confusion on these and indeed all other matters of inquiry, by formulating a test by which we could distinguish the false from the true; or at least a certain necessary condition to which all evidence on whatever subject must conform, if it is to be valid. What this condition is, he gathers from the example of a narrowly limited field of inquiry; indeed he could have come by the suggestion had he had nothing before him but Euclid's Elements. Montaigne had complained that among the most widely accepted opinions held by man, he could find not "one alone that was not impugned or disallowed, not by one nation, but by many." Yet here was a whole system of propositions, accepted by all men of all times capable of understanding them and the evidence on which they rested. But then Montaigne, landed proprietor, burgomaster of Bordeaux, had been looking for practical principles, moral laws; and of these he could find none that were of general acceptance. Descartes, philosopher, was seeking certainties wherever he could find them; and it would have been strange if Descartes, mathematician, originator of analytical geometry, should not have found them in the principles of mathematics, "on account," as he says, "of the evidence and certitude of their reasoning." But what is the reason of the difference between the conflicting opinions men held concerning the principles of morality, and the unanimity of their acceptance of the propositions of mathematics? The reason lay in the different kinds of evidence on which they respectively rested: practical principles were dependent on mathematical evidence entirely independent of the evidence of the senses and of the feelings.

Here, then, is the first principle of the test by which we could distinguish the true from the false, the necessary condition to which all evidence must conform: to be valid, it must be free of all dependence on the testimony of our senses and our feelings. And history showed that evidence fulfilling this condition could be gathered in sufficient detail to answer quite a range of questions in which men are interested; the range, namely, covered by the sciences we now call formal: logic, arithmetic, geometry. But, by taking thought, could we not widen the spread of questions covered by formal science? Could we not expand it to include, if not in fact yet in promise, all meaningful questions man could ask? That is what Rationalism undertook to think out.

Descartes set himself to show that just this could be done, at least for a range of questions comparable in scope to those included in a classic *De Rerum Natura*. The *Principia* presents a system of sciences which build up from a mechanics through a mechanistic biology to an equally mechanistic psychology of the emotions. True, the consistency of this generally mechanistic interpretation of nature was interrupted by the exemption of man, in his more rational moments of knowing and doing, from the control of that mechanical law which determined the course of all closed natural systems devoid of human participation in their history. The incongruity of this nature image in which mechanistic and vitalistic motives were brought into impossible partnership was promptly recognized and corrected by Descartes' immediate followers Spinoza and Leibnitz; the former adhering to a consistently mechanistic, the latter developing, in his monad-theory, an equally consistent vitalistic nature image. And with this page in which appear two separately self-consistent, but mutually incompatible nature-images, Rationalism's offering of a *De Rerum Natura*, based on what purported to be purely formal evidence, ended.

But one who supposed the history of a philosophy to be adequately told by what the historian of philosophy records of its major figures would miss much that a more general type of historian would consider the most important contribution of that school. The historian of philosophy very properly limits himself to those thinkers who had exhausted all that history has to show of the fundamental applications of a given method. On one or another of these foundations, later members of the school build this or that special structure. With these details our historian is not interested, but turns his attention to the next offering in the way of a theory of evidence. Where the interest of the historian of philosophy ends, that of the culture-historian begins; and did we follow such an historian through his review of the seventeenth and eighteenth centuries' thought, we should find the influence of rationalism to have shaped the doctrine of every special theorist: sociologist, economist, political scientist, jurisconsult, aesthetician—down, if you please, to the theorist of architecture. Of which matters, we find all that had been developed to his day gathered together with encyclopedic completeness in the system of Christian Wolff (1659–1754) with such thoroughness that the Leibnitzo-Wolffian text became the standard teaching of the universities of the continent down to and well beyond the student days of Immanuel Kant.

Throughout this period, one sees how reciprocal was the helpfulness of the general to the special and of the special to the general theorist: the tools of evidence established by the one furnish the other with a *modus inveniendi* he had hitherto lacked; the successful gathering of evidence conforming with these requirements in more and more varied fields of special inquiry confirms the founders' hope that evidence meeting the strict conditions their school imposed upon validity could be collected in sufficient detail to answer every meaningful question humanity could put to itself. If this triumphant spread of Rationalistic method had met with no subsequent disappointment, the history of philosophy would have ended with Rationalism; but it did not, and the reason it did not is the same in kind with that which caused the downfall of every subsequent theory of evidence which, having had its day in the sun, passed into history and was replaced by what promised to be a less vulnerable successor. The fatal moment comes when a critical mind is forced to realize that there is one or another class of questions that cannot be looked upon as meaningless, yet to which no answer based on evidence consistent with the demands of the school can be returned.

One would suppose a question whose insolubility had passed unnoted by the searching mind of a continent for well over a century to have lain, for the most part, in some very remote field of human interest, there to lie undiscovered by any but some very special kind of investigator. Such, however, is not the history of things: neither in the instance of Rationalism, nor in any subsequent case of a question whose insolubility proved the undoing of a widely accepted theory of evidence, is the fatal question at all recondite. The death of old and birth of new schools is not consequent on any new discovery, but on a new reflection, one in which it is realized that a whole class of familiar questions that had supposedly been answered consistently with a certain theory of evidence had not in fact been so answered. In the case of Rationalism, the class of questions affected by such a reflection was no less than the whole class of questions of fact. How could it have been supposed that all such questions were answerable on the purely formal evidence to which Rationalism restricted itself, and how this illusion was lifted, is more quickly told if we accept the definition of Rationalism as it comes completed from the pen of Leibnitz, the last general theorist to formulate that theory, rather than as it was left imperfectly defined by his predecessors, Descartes and Spinoza.

For Descartes had left the criterion of validity in purely negative form: valid evidence must not depend on the testimony of the senses. Not that Descartes or the later Rationalists failed to value the new science so rapidly developing in their century: the essentially experimental

science of Galileo, Brahe, Kepler, Torricelli, Huygens, all of whom de-
pended for their data on sense and manifold observation. Descartes in
particular was so impressed with the results obtained by these observers
that he urged all who had the leisure to devote themselves to such observations and inductions as might add new detail to the world-image
the pioneer experimenters had fashioned. But the Rationalists valued
these experimental findings only for their suggestiveness; not for their
ultimate authority. Experimental inductions held greater promise of
being later established as deductions than did proposals coming from
any other source. But these proposals were not to be accepted as true
propositions until such deductions were forthcoming, i.e., until, after
the manner of the propositions of arithmetic and geometry, they had
been shown to follow from premises independent of empirical evidence,
and so shown by a logic no less independent of experience.

But if the propositions of such a system of sciences did not depend on
empirical evidence for their certainty, on what kind of evidence did they
depend? This was the question that forerunners of Leibnitz generally
left unasked, and always unanswered. With Leibnitz comes the definite
asking and answering of the question, together with the reason why the
answer given by him must be the only answer possible to a Rationalistic
theory of evidence. The premises of all established science must be definitions, and definitions only; for, as Leibnitz says, "these depend solely
on ourselves and have no need of other support (*n'ont que faire de
secours extérieurs*)." How seriously he means this pronouncement is
seen from the way in which he takes Euclid himself to task for having
included among the premises of his geometry, beside definitions, axioms
("common notions") and postulates that are neither definitions nor
shown to be deducible from definitions. "The same motives," says Leibnitz, "that would make Euclid try to prove that two sides of a triangle are
greater than the third (although the truth of this is so evident to experience that, as the ancients jokingly said, even asses recognize it in not
taking round-about roads to their mangers)—the motive, namely, that
Euclid wanted geometrical truths to depend, not on sense-images but
on reason—these same motives would make one wish to prove that two
straights can intersect at only one point, which Euclid could have proved
si bonam rectae definitionem habuisset." (*Animadversiones in partem
generalem Principiorum Cartesianorum.*)

With this, the thesis of Rationalism is completely defined, its meaning and intent made unequivocally clear. But with the certainty of its
meaning comes the certainty of its fate: it is impossible for any but one
infatuated with the lofty but impossible dream of an absolutely certain,
non-empirical science, long to escape the conclusion that no science

founded on definitions alone could answer a single question of fact. Who would pretend that from the definition of a triangle or of an equilateral chiliagon one could learn whether or not there was in fact such a thing as a triangle or an equilateral chiliagon? Nor would the rationalizers themselves ever have thought otherwise, had they not, under the spell of their dream, argued themselves into the conviction, first, that there was after all one definition from which one could deduce the existence of an object of the kind defined; and, second, that from this one definitionally established fact, the answer to every other question of fact could be deduced.

The one definition from which an individual existence could be deduced was the definition of God. This definition they accepted at the hands of the eleventh-century schoolman St. Anselm, as also the argument to show that from his definition followed the existence of God. That argument was the famous ontological argument for the existence of God: God is a most perfect being; a most perfect being has all possible attributes; one possible attribute is existence; ergo, etc.

This argument and its conclusion is the common property of the Rationalist school: not so the argument obviously needed to show how from the existence of this divine individual could be deduced the existence or nonexistence of the sun that to the eyes of all shines at noon; or the fly that to my lone ear buzzes by at the moment. On these topics, Descartes and Spinoza hold their thought in reserve. They could not doubt, without admitting to their counsel evidence of the senses, that sufficiently clear thinking should be able to deduce the truth or error of all the opinions we now uncertainly hold on no other testimony than that of our senses. But it is not until we come to Leibnitz that we find a concerted effort to think these things out. It is Leibnitz, once more, who risks his neck by coming down to facts. A most perfect being (he argues) would lack something of perfection were he anything less than the sufficient reason for the being of everything that is; and he would fall short of perfection were he anything less than good enough to make a world, for whose every detail he was the sole reason, the best of all possible worlds. In this line of argument, whose conclusions he sketched only in bold outline, Leibnitz was followed by the minor prophets of the school, filling in his outline with that elaborate detail one finds in the aforementioned volumes of Wolff.

Now, as has been said, only minds under the spell of the rationalistic vision of a science free from dependence on the illusory testimony of sense could have rested content for a moment, let alone for a century and more, with any such argument as this. The world outside this devoted fold of visionaries did not have to wait for the profundities of a

Kant to sense the weakness of the ontological proof; it did not have to wait for the ironic pen of a Voltaire to see the absurdity of picturing the sorry affair men live in as the best of all possible worlds. Long before Kant's *Kritik* of 1781 had demolished the ontological proof; well before Voltaire's *Candide* of 1759 had reduced the best of all possible worlds to a figure of laughter, had appeared a work largely responsible for both; Locke's *Essay* of 1695. It laid the foundations of a theory of evidence denying everything Rationalism had asserted, asserting everything Rationalism had denied. It was the theory known as eighteenth-century Empiricism. For it, there was nothing to trust to but the evidence of the senses; nothing so empty of either truth or error as a formal science deduced from man-made premises, each introduced by Euclid's word *postuletur* and properly therefore to be called *postulates* or *proposals*.

Now, this newer Empiricism, like the older Rationalism, was born of a critical mind's dissatisfaction with the opinions of its day, based as they were on patently specious evidence. And as once the mind of Descartes, so now the mind of Locke, saves itself from all-doubting skepticism by accepting as sound the evidence on which a limited class of inquirers were answering their special class of questions. Only, whereas Descartes put his trust in the oldest of sciences, Locke pinned his faith to the newest. For Locke belonged to the end, as Descartes to the beginning of a century that "reflected the glory of Kepler and Newton," and had he been a physicist he would certainly have drawn his principal inspiration from these great masters of induction based on manifold observation. But Locke was not a physicist; he was a physician, the year-long friend and collaborator of a practitioner who laid the foundation of modern medicine in what we should now call clinical observation and induction: Sydenham. This makes it probable, and his conception of science makes it more so, that the science in whose evidence Locke's critical mind found the satisfaction that was refused it elsewhere was even narrower in the range of questions with which it coped than the cosmos-sweeping physics of Galileo, Kepler, and Newton.

The rest of the story of Empiricism parallels that of Rationalism; from equally narrow, though vastly different beginnings, both Descartes and Locke set out to generalize; both essay to make available for the answering of all meaningful questions the kind of evidence they find sound and adequate for the answering of some; both are followed by generally approving, but occasionally critical and emending minds: as Descartes by Spinoza and Leibnitz, so Locke by Berkeley and Hume. From both emanate influences that dominate thought on all important issues for a century or more; as from Descartes stems the cultural period called

Rationalism, so from Locke, the period of Enlightenment. Both developments end in encyclopedias, the Rationalist in that of Wolff; the Enlightenment in that known to all later history as *The Encyclopedia*. The world is not likely to forget how hopefully the Enlightenment uplifted the hearts, how tragically the Encyclopedia engulfed the lives of all subject to their influence.

Here let this hasty sketch of the history of modern thought end before it runs on to immodest length, as it surely would were it to follow to the end the trend of reflection it sets going. It is not, to be sure, a critically convincing argument for the likeness of four lives, to have sketched only the first, then swept the others vaguely in with an *ab uno disce omnes*. Yet, within its limits of time and space, the present paper can do no more, by way of rounding out its thought, than put a double question: the first addressed to those who have in mind the past; the second, to those who have at heart the future of things.

Of the first, then, I ask, Do you not find that of the four schools under which the movements of modern thought may be classified, the first three conform to a common pattern of coming into being and passing away; to which the fourth also conforms in all but the manner of a death that has not yet overtaken it? Have not all lived through a sequence of similar moments? In the first, a critical mind is troubled either by the conflict of beliefs prevailing in its day, or by an all too prevalent harmony, based upon the common acceptance of an all too specious evidence. In a second, this scrupulous intellect saves itself from the waste of universal, irresoluble doubt, by accepting as well enough proven a limited range of opinions supported by evidence strong enough to withstand the criticism that has thrown into doubt all evidence other than this. A third moment finds this mind, having lived through specious negation and found room for limited affirmation, trying to enlarge its living room. It essays generalization; it asks itself whether all the questions man may reasonably ask cannot be answered one way or the other on evidence of this convincing kind. (It makes no difference, by the way, whether this generalizing mind answer its own question affirmatively [as did the Rationalist and Empiricist of our example] or negatively [as we should have found Kant to have done, had our review of the past gone so far]. It is the generality of the question, not the simplicity of the answer that makes the philosopher and marks his influence. No doubt Kant, in the spirit of that parsimony which is the very genius of science, would have preferred to find the experimental method that sufficed to answer the demands of natural science, adequate to resolve the issues of morals and religion. But he could not; he could only give patent reason why he could not. Now one may not think this body of reasoning to be the most valuable of Kant's contributions to philosophy, but one cannot deny it to have been the most influential in stirring the thought of its day and many a day thereafter.) But to continue with the life-cycle of the schools: a fourth moment in the career of any one of them is reached when the generalizing mind of its founder shall have so justified its findings in the eyes of a sufficiently wide world as to have set the minds of a world of specialists to answering their specific questions in terms of the one theory of evidence. This practical application of such a theory is the laboratory test of its soundness; not necessarily because one or another kind of specialist will have found pitfalls among the questions specific to his field of inquiry; but, generally, because the working of many minds upon an issue of evidence multiplies the chances that defects, obvious enough when pointed out, will have been uncovered by the sheer vigor of a general agitation of the question. And, to those of us who consider Rationalism, Empiricism, Criticism to be theories that have had their day and passed away, the reason of their passing is always the same: a class of questions, generally a very broad if not all-inclusive range of questions, supposedly answered by the methods approved of a school outlived, are seen not to have been answered; or else to have been answered on the basis of evidence not conforming to the requirements of that school. How the death of Rationalism followed on the recognition of its impotence to answer the simplest question of fact, we have already seen. The Empiricism that corrected this fault, by giving not only some but all-inclusive place to observation in establishing both matters of fact and matters of law, fell in its turn before the criticism of Kant; a criticism that pointed out, what every experimental scientist knows, that science can respond to questions neither of fact nor law until it shall have adjusted the ultimate data of its observation to a formal pattern; a pattern, as Kant quite saw, whose space-time coördinates should individuate its facts, and whose law should establish a cause-effect relation between successive distributions of these facts. If, finally, Kant's critical philosophy succumbed to the argument of twentieth-century Experimentalism, it is because Criticism proved inadequate to exhaust the meaning of experimental method. It is not surprising that Kant did not see, what no one began to see till a good half-century after his death; namely, that other geometries than the Euclidian, other types of law than the Newtonian, were available for the construction of those formal patterns, to one or another, not as Kant thought to just one of which observational data must be adjusted if experimental evidence is to respond to questions whether of fact or of law. This is one of the comparatively rare instances in which a general theory of evidence was not invalidated but liberalized and made more general through the very special studies of very special scientists.

So much for the first of my two questions: if those who know the past give it an affirmative answer, I have little doubt of the answer those who think of the future will give to the second. For if indeed it be admitted that the most important schools of thought, through which humanity has passed in its progress toward a sound theory of evidence, have themselves passed through the critical moments here supposed to chart their common course, then nothing could be more apparent than the traditional service rendered each to each by general theorist and special investigator, sharing the day between them. That they could be thus cooperative, results from a condition common to all the days these laborers have shared or shall ever come to share. Unlike as may be the tasks on which we should find the random philosopher and the random specialist engaged at any random moment, these two workmen must in all their moments have one problem in common: to gain a progressively critical insight into what constitutes evidence. And this insight neither could gain without the help of the other. Is there then any doubt as to the answer to be given my second question? But I need not word it; it words itself, and with this answer stands explained one of the sayings with which this discussion opened; namely, that your coöperationist, whether philosopher or scientist, considers himself to be the true traditionalist and conservative: each abides in the unchanging course set by the connotation of his calling. Not that either need deny to his isolationist colleague the right to call himself conservative in another sense: the denotation of philosophy and the denotation of science or of any other special discipline will doubtless find the general theorist and the special investigator daily absorbed in activities as remote from one another as you please. Noting this remoteness of detail, your isolationist loses sight of the identity of a thread on which all successful details must be strung: it is the thread of sound evidence. In better assuring the soundness and extending the length of this thread, your philosopher concerned with what is evidence, and your investigator seeking what is evident, have a common interest. It is an interest best served by the constant and conscious collaboration of the two.

And this might be taken as the answer your coöperationist philosopher of any school would return to the isolationist question, "How comes it that certain philosophers have been active in organizing, other philosophers interested in following, a symposium in which general theorist and special investigator join in offering for their common consideration the results of their several studies?" But if the coöperationist to whom this question is addressed be of the Experimentalist school, his answer can be more specific than that based on the lesson of a past common to all schools, though it can be offered here only in terms of some brief example. Of a host of such examples, let me choose one in which the philosopher compares the grasp we have, in two different cases, on the meaning of two terms that have been central in the philosopher's thought for many a century: appearance and reality. In one case, we ask, "What does a man really weigh;" in the second, "What does a man really want?" In the first case, experimental science has put the philosopher in a way to see clearly enough the meaning of the two correlatives, apparent and real weight. For science, the apparent has become the approximate; the real, that which is approximated to. But this correlation might still be vague and verbal, were it not that science has long been in position to measure the difference between any given approach to the real, and the real that is approached. For something like a century and a half, science has been able to assign to each of its approximations a definite order; indicated, let us say, by the order of the last decimal place to which science regards its approximation as significant. To approach a step closer to the real, your experimenter must find a way of advancing from an approximation of the nth to one of the $(n + 1)$th order. But no approximation of however high an order determines what digits shall fill decimal places of higher order than its last. Yet we understand the real distance in question to be some one number of the number system, its digits determinate in all decimal places to infinity. No finite experiment can find this number; science can never find the real. No; science cannot *find,* but so long as the way of progressive approximation is open to it, it can *define* the real of which it knows the appearance: for it, the real is the limiting conception of the goal approached by an approximation as the order of approximation is raised without limit. The appearance this reality presents to science at any finite stage of its progress is an approximation of such order as science may have established at that stage.

Compare, if you will, the clarity of this correlation between appearance and reality, with the obscurity that clouds the meaning of these correlatives as they enter into our second question, "What does a man really want?" The obscurity is equally dense whether the man in question be a given man, or that much-discussed person, the average, or random man. To be sure, there have been, there are philosophies that see no obscurity here. All these philosophies suppose the question to be answerable in one way or another. If you want to know what your neighbor really wants, why not ask him? He must surely be able and, if willing and honest, ready to inform you as to his wants no less definitely than you could inform yourself of your own wants, if you asked yourself about them. As to the average man, there have been volumes of the most practical bearing on human affairs, that start right off with the certainty that what this person really wants is to sustain his life and propagate his kind. For such philosophies, a real want, so far from being hard to define, is none too difficult to find. On the other hand, your Experimentalist philosopher is so corrupted by his habit of listening to the conversation of experimental scientists, as to conceive it no more possible to find out what your random man, your neighboring man, or you yourself really want, than it is to find out for any of these characters the real distance from the top of his head to the soles of his feet. But at least in speaking of the latter reality, he knows what he means. Is he in like case when he speaks of the former? He will be, if experimental method can find a way of establishing an approximation to man's real want of an order no less determinate than that ascribed to its approximation to his height. Can experimental science go to such lengths as this? If not, of two things the one. Either experimental evidence cannot fulfill the philosopher's parsimonious hope that such evidence is the only evidence needed to satisfy the questioning mind of man. Either this, or our philosophy must acknowledge it meaningless to ask what any man, not excluding oneself, really wants.

Now suppose your Experimentalist philosopher with this question on his mind, or any one of numberless others like it, were to run across a program in which it was announced that at a certain symposium a number of special investigators were to discuss what they have found or were trying to find as to (I consult the program) *Ways of Evaluating Preferences, The Meaning of Measurement, Specifications for Consumer Goods, Application of Measurements of Interests, Preferences, and Attitudes.*

Suppose, I ask, such a philosopher to come across such a program, What do you think he's going to do about it?

SOME CRITERIA FOR JUDGING THE QUALITY OF SURVEYS
By
W. EDWARDS DEMING

I

IN MY own work it has seemed useful to recognize two general types of sample-design. The distinction I wish to draw is defined by whether the sampling plan controls the biases of selection, nonresponse, and estimation, and furnishes a measure of the sampling tolerance (these terms will be described in Part III). Thus there are:

1. Quantitative surveys, wherein the biases of selection, nonresponse, and estimation are under control and the sampling plan furnishes a measure of the sampling tolerance.

2. Qualitative surveys, wherein the reliability cannot be calculated from the sample but by the judgment of experts.

I am not enamored of the overworked adjectives "quantitative" and "qualitative" in this connection, and must ask the reader to regard them only as labels whose meanings are defined above for my special purpose. In this sense a survey may be classed as qualitative if it is liable to the biases of selection or nonresponse, and if the sampling tolerance cannot be computed. Thus it is qualitative if it depends on 1. a judgment or quota selection of "typical" areas, road-segments, blocks, households, firms, or farms; or 2. the interviewer's judgment concerning a representative selection of households or establishments; or 3. the evaluation of incomplete responses (as from a mailed questionnaire); or even 4. the evaluation of responses, even if complete, from a selected mailing list.

There are reasons for not using the terms "purposive selection" and "case histories" to designate qualitative surveys; purposive selection has long denoted a selection of counties or cities, but with never a reference to the method of selection of blocks, road-segments, households, farms, or firms within the county or city. Case histories, on the other hand, are often extensive explorations of households or other small units. Hence a new name is needed and I have adopted an overworked adjective as being preferable to one with too definite connotations.

On the other hand, a procedure of survey may be classed as quantitative 1. if it eliminates or at least controls the biases of selection, estimation, and nonresponse, and 2. if it permits advance calculation of the sampling tolerance. Such a procedure is often spoken of as unbiased, but I have adopted the adjective "quantitative" for this particular discourse. One reason for deciding against the term "unbiased" for quantitative surveys is that I am unwilling to say that every qualitative survey is biased. The question is not one of bias but of the amount of bias and how the reliability is to be determined.

The reliability of a qualitative survey is subjective, being decided by the judgment of experts (which would of course include experts in the subject-matter as well as statisticians). On the other hand, the reliability of a quantitative survey is objective, being furnished and guaranteed by the plan itself. In case the experts disagree, the reliability of a qualitative survey is undecided, and until resolved must be considered unattained. It is the resolution of just this difficulty that constitutes the main argument in favor of a quantitative survey, and which has so greatly stimulated research in sampling. Incidentally, this research is doing as much for qualitative methods as for quantitative methods.

When the experts agree that a particular survey, though subject to quantitatively unmeasurable bias and sampling error, will still provide the desired information with the reliability required, and do so cheaper than any other approach, then the qualitative survey should certainly be regarded as proper. On the other hand, there are circumstances wherein it is essential to have quantitative results—i.e., freedom from the biases of selection and nonresponse and a sampling tolerance furnished unequivocally by the sample itself, and thus removed from judgment. Such is the case in many government surveys, where figures guide important decisions affecting prices, wages, health programs, agricultural production and forecasts, relief programs, and many other governmental policies. Likewise in market research and public opinion: occasions are arising in which important decisions should be arrived at only on consideration of figures possessing known and objectively determinable reliability.

It is important to recognize the similarities and differences between the two general approaches to sample-design, and to be aware of the advantages, disadvantages, and limitations of each. The two approaches are similar so far as the questionnaire and instructions are concerned; their differences lie purely in the sampling procedure, hence in the control or lack of control in the biases of selection, estimation, and nonresponse, and in the possibility of computing the sampling tolerance. Considerations of the validity of the data do not enter: the distinction is purely whether the reliability is objectively computable. It follows that there is no distinction when a complete coverage is made—i.e., when the sample is 100 per cent.

Some surveys should be qualitative and some should be quantitative. Both types have inherent merit. In my own practice I certainly use both. It would be futile to try to make a list of circumstances wherein either type should be used because each case must be carefully considered. Attached to each problem are certain aims, requirements in reliability, limitation of funds, time, professional staff, maps, lists, and other considerations and resources peculiar to this particular problem. It is possible nevertheless to make some pretty definite statements as a basis for considerations of adequacy. In the first place, whatever design can provide the information and required reliability at the lowest cost is the proper one, regardless of tradition or how it is labeled. In the second place, a sample-design is not to be considered adequate or proper simply because it is the best one that can be devised under the circumstances. Something more should be required, namely, that it shall provide the information and reliability that are specified; else it should not be taken at all. This statement implies an element of prediction: it must be possible to say *in advance* that a plan is adequate, or that it provides a framework that can be expanded to adequacy. This is so because if the adequacy of a survey cannot be asserted in advance, in terms of the required specifications of reliability (*vide infra*), neither can it be afterward, because unfortunately comparisons between sample-results and census or other known data do not by themselves constitute acceptable verification.

I think that some misunderstanding has arisen and that it will continue to retard progress in sampling unless cleared up, which explains the purpose of this article. The basis for this misunderstanding lies not so much in failure to recognize the importance of biases and sampling errors as in failure to appreciate how easily biases can arise, and in failure to recognize the fact that a qualitative survey has merit in its own right when properly used. The last-named misunderstanding manifests itself in attempts to dress up qualitative surveys in the language and style of quantitative surveys, more concerning which will be mentioned further on.

The discourse that follows necessarily deals largely with the question of reliability—how reliability is judged and, in particular, under what circumstances the reliability of a survey is computable in the quantitative sense.

II

A statistical program must possess five characteristics: comprehensiveness, uniformity, speed, reliability, and validity.

Comprehensiveness is necessary for correct interpretation. For guidance on economic programs, for example, the usefulness of data on production is certainly enhanced by the existence of data on distribution and consumption.

Uniformity of definitions, procedures, units and measures, and reporting dates is necessary; otherwise interpretation of the figures may be impossible or misleading.

Speed. Data must be timely. If the figures come in too late, action will be taken without them and their value is largely lost. Statistical programs must be planned in advance, so that figures are not merely a historical record by the time they are published.

Reliability. You can't use figures if you can't trust their representativeness.

Validity. You can't use figures unless they represent answers to the questions that you think they answer. In other words, you want the right answers to the right questions.

All five of these requirements are well recognized and admitted. The need for speed and for reliability and validity have given ascendancy to two important angles of specialization in the statistical profession—1. the construction of questionnaires and technique of interviewing, and 2. the design of samples. The construction of questionnaires and the technique of interviewing are special provinces of overlap between the statistician, psychologist, and expert in the subject-matter involved (population, agriculture, irrigation, retailer of clothing, public health, or some other subject), the aim of their endeavors being to elicit valid answers. In other words, their aim is to avoid the fifth and sixth biases in the list given in Part IV, and thus to elicit answers that will be correctly interpreted. The design of samples, on the other hand, is basically mathematical, requiring coöperation between the mathematical statistician and an expert in the subject-matter, with the aim of improving reliability and decreasing costs. Of course the same man may serve in all these capacities, and frequently does, but it is convenient to separate his functions. Actually I should hazard a guess that 90 per cent of the time of the mathematical statisticians that I know goes toward the construction of questionnaires and techniques of interviewing; nevertheless it is the importance of reliability that I wish to stress especially on this occasion where the aim is to distinguish between qualitative and quantitative surveys.

Reliability and validity should not be confused. The problems of validity exist in exactly the same way whether the survey is total or a small sample. The question of what size sample to use or how to take it does not come up until the problems of validity have been met and successfully conquered—the questionnaire, instructions, tabulation plans, and all that sort of consideration. Many a proposed survey never gets as far as the sampling stage.

Honesty and good intentions are not enough in sample-design. It is necessary to be aware of the weaknesses, limitations, advantages and disadvantages of different methods, thus not to get fooled into false confidence. Intuition, like the conscience, must be trained. In particular, intuition is not a good guide in sampling unless the intuition is trained by mathematical insight. It is a fact that untrained intuition has led unsuspectingly to the use of biased methods and inefficient practice in some statistical work. For example—and it may be astounding—a sure way toward bias in many types of inquiry is to leave to the judgment of an expert or to the interviewer, however competent and well-meaning, the selection of "representative" or "typical" areas, road-segments, blocks, households, firms, or farms.

III

Wrong data often lead to wrong and costly decisions. An understanding of reliability and sampling variability is therefore important to the consumers of data, and it should not be necessary to apologize for introducing some concepts that contribute toward an understanding of these things, even though these concepts lie outside the pale of everyday discourse.

The first step in the concept of reliability is the recognition of two kinds of errors—biases and sampling variability. Too much of either one can invalidate a survey, and thus lead to wrong decisions. Bias and sampling variability are different in nature, as shown by the chart further on. The insidious thing about biases is their constancy and the difficulty of detecting them. Thus, if a survey is repeated time and again according to some specified procedure, the biases remain essentially constant and undetected. This statement leads to some corollaries that are frequently overlooked. To be specific, if the results of a large survey are divided into ten piles at random, or are divided up according to geographic location of the regions whence they originate, intercomparisons are incapable of detecting a bias in the overall procedure, because the results in each pile may *all be wrong by the same amount*. Similarly, agreement year after year does not demonstrate the absence of a bias. Rather such differences are manifestations of sampling variability.

It should be remarked also that a bias is not removed or even diminished by increasing the size of sample, there being one exception—bias arising from the method of selecting the areas and households for the sample is reduced toward zero if the size of sample is increased to the neighborhood of 100 per cent. Another remark may be of interest at

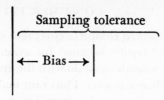

METHOD A
Heavy bias; wide sampling tolerances

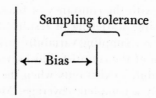

METHOD B
Heavy bias; narrow sampling tolerances

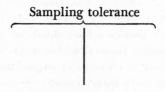

METHOD C
Negligible bias; wide sampling tolerances

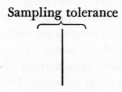

METHOD D
Negligible bias; narrow sampling tolerances
111

this point: repeated complete coverages should not be expected to produce identical results because, for example, even the vagaries of the weather have something to do with the answers obtained in a household interview such as a census. Thus rain may keep certain people at home to give information to the interviewer, whereas in clear weather the response would have come from someone else in the family and might have been very different. Moreover, the weather may easily affect the response obtained from any given person. Similarly, a magnetic storm would affect the answers obtained in a radio survey, whether complete coverage or sample.

Contrasting with the constancy of biases, sampling variability is disclosed by a visible scattering of results about a center of gravity as a survey is repeated. Sampling variability arises from accidental variations in the selection of the counties, blocks, road-segments, households, etc. Sampling variability exists only when the coverage is less than total; it is wiped out by a complete coverage. Moreover, sampling variability exists whether the biases are appreciable or negligible.

In order to say whether a procedure of survey yields too much bias, or whether it yields negligible bias, it is necessary to have a scientific measure of bias, and a similar statement holds for sampling variability.

One of the simplest illustrations of bias and sampling variability is found in shots aimed at a target. The target might be the vertical line seen in the chart. If the center of gravity of your shots falls to the right, as in the two top panels, there is a bias which can be corrected by changing the setting of the sights. In surveys, a bias can be corrected by changing the method of survey, such as by changing the method of selecting the households that are to be interviewed, or by calling back (again and again if necessary) on people not at home at first call instead of omitting them or making substitutions. There is another very important characteristic of repeated shots; they do not all fall at the same spot; there is a scatter, even with a fixed setting of the sights. This scatter corresponds to sampling variability.

In the chart are four panels illustrating the different degrees of bias and sampling variability that are produced by different types of sample design. In the top panel heavy biases are present. One contributory bias might be the bias of selection—as for example exists when the interviewer's judgment is allowed to come into play (mentioned earlier), or when nothing is done to elicit responses from people who are not at home at first call, or who mislay their questionnaires. The sampling variability in the top panel is wide but this is under control; it can be made narrower (as in Panel B) by increasing the size of sample or introducing more effective stratification or more efficient methods of estimation. In Panel C the biases have practically all been removed, as by automatic selection and energetic follow-up of nonresponse, or correction by other devices, but the sampling tolerance is wide. In Panel D the sampling tolerance of Panel C above has been narrowed, again possibly by increasing the size of sample or making other suitable modifications in procedure.

It is important to note that sampling variability has the property of possessing a range or tolerance, as indicated in the chart. The sampling tolerance is a band outside of which practically no shots ever fall. *It is impossible to predict a hit* other than to say that it will fall *inside the sampling tolerance.* However, *it is possible to control the width of the sampling tolerance.* In shooting, the scatter (tolerance) is controlled by the quality, design, and uniformity of the ammunition, length of barrel, and in other ways. In surveys, the sampling tolerance can be made large or small by regulating the size of the sample (i.e., the number of households in it) and the way in which it is drawn and the way the estimates are calculated. By making the sample 100 per cent, i.e., by covering all the households in the country, the sampling variability would be reduced to zero. However, in most surveys the expense of a complete coverage is far too great, and moreover the job often becomes so enormous that the results, by the time they are ready, are well-nigh useless, being only a historical record. What is more, the bigger the job, the more liable it is to biases of various kinds that creep in and become troublesome. The bigger the job the more difficult it is to control, and the less selective one may be in the choice of the personnel required, and the less effective becomes any sort of training program. Many a small sample has been preferable to an attempted complete coverage. Large surveys like the Decennial Census of Population or the Census of Agriculture or a five-year Census of Business need to be complete, but they would be worthless without elaborate preparation and proper facilities. Of course there are instances, which we in the sampling profession see every day, wherein the number of members to be covered, even in total, is so few that the simplest and cheapest sample by which to achieve the desired accuracy is a complete coverage: some industries, for example, are concentrated into a very few large corporations or companies.

For reasons that may be apparent from the foregoing material, the practicable and necessary size of a survey is usually limited. In every problem in which information is desired, there is a permissible range of sampling variability within which no further precision is useful, but only represents wasted funds and effort. For example, in the population count of a city, or zone, a precision of better than a 1 per cent coefficient of variation, corresponding to a sampling tolerance of 3 per cent, is ordinarily not required, because precision better than 3 per cent is no better than an exact count in making decisions in problems of public health, allocation of food, size and number of retail outlets required, type of advertising, and many other decisions. The problem in quantitative sample-design is therefore to meet the requirement in sampling tolerance, but *only to meet it and no more,* and to do so at the lowest possible cost. The problem cannot be solved unless the biases and sampling variability are under control, which implies that the sampling tolerance must be computable *in advance.* In a professional job of sampling, the expected width of the sampling tolerance is always computable as part of the sampling plan. This means that the risk of sampling is not a matter of guesswork, but is ascertainable and under control.

Two further remarks concerning the chart, before leaving this section. First, like most illustrations it is oversimplified. Almost every sample actually consists of several samples—as many as there are questions to be tabulated, whereas the chart applies to any one question, but to only one at a time. In sample-design it is necessary to plan the sample so that the required reliability is obtained in whichever question is most difficult to attain with the desired precision. Thus, in a sample that is intended to produce a population count as well as population characteristics, the design would ordinarily be laid out along lines that will produce the required reliability in the population count (such as a standard error of 1 per cent), because a sample that will do this will yield more reliability than is usually required for characteristics such as age-distribution in five-year age classes, the sex ratio, school attendance, classes of employment and unemployment, marital status, and other characteristics for which ordinarily only proportions in broad classes are desired.

Second, on many occasions checks on samples are provided by comparison with census data or some other survey using suitably similar definitions and approaches. It is a curious thing to note, however, that the statistician is singularly unimpressed of such comparisons. The reason is that he must know *in advance* to what degree he has controlled the biases of selection and nonresponse, and he must know *in advance* the width of his sampling tolerance. It is therefore no astonishment to him to learn that his sample agrees within so many per cent of a complete count. He knows, moreover, that instances of remarkably close agreement are mere accidents, and again he is not impressed. He thinks in terms of a distribution of results, with a sampling tolerance.

IV

Biases can and do arise from many sources, some of which are listed below: [1]

1. Bias arising from the method of selecting the respondents (the main topic of this discourse)
2. Bias of an unrepresentative date for the survey (not essentially different from the bias just mentioned)
3. Bias of the estimating procedure
4. Bias of nonresponse

   The people who do not respond to a mailed questionnaire deserve representation. A professional job of sampling contains provision for a face-to-face interview of a subsample of the people who do not return their questionnaires. Similarly, in a survey carried out by interviews, some provision must be made for calling on a proper sample of people not at home at first call, or who refused.
5. Bias of the questionnaire
6. Bias arising from errors in response

   Bias injected by the type of inquiry (mail, interview, invitational questionnaire)

   Bias injected by the interviewer

   Bias injected by the auspices (protection of self-interest)

   Mistakes in response, intentional and unintentional

   Understating age, or rounding to the nearest 5: up-grading the husband's occupation or education; failure of memory

Regarding the bias of selection (first-mentioned above), a few words may be inserted at this point. As is well recognized, information obtained from one segment of the population may not be valid for another segment. For example, ascription of the characteristics of telephone homes to non-telephone homes may lead to serious mistakes in marketing and other practice. Likewise, ascription of the characteristics and opinions of the people interviewed to the people not interviewed is dangerous if the selection of the sample has been accomplished by expert judgment or the fulfillment of quotas, because such procedures put certain biases of selection to work. In the hope of avoiding errors of this kind, and at the same time to narrow the sampling tolerances, controls in the form of stratification are sometimes introduced, such as control by geographic location, degree of urbanization, and other character-

[1] A more detailed list of the different kinds of errors that afflict surveys is contained in an article entitled "On Errors in Surveys" in the *American Sociological Review*, IX (1944), 359–69.

istics. Such devices may or may not have much effect. Unfortunately again, the untrained intuition is a poor guide. The fact is that no amount of stratification can take the place of proper procedures of selection of households from within strata. The answer is determined not alone by the stratification and controls (which may indeed be helpful), but rather by *the method of selecting the elements* (areas, road-segments, blocks, households, firms, or farms) *from within the strata.*

Three of the main biases (viz., the bias of the method of selecting the respondents, the bias of nonresponse, and the bias of the estimating procedure) are under control *provided* certain procedures are carried out. These procedures require that *all elements* of the universe (as of households, firms, or farms or other areas) must have a chance of getting into the sample. Moreover, *these chances must be known* because they figure in the estimating techniques by which the final tables are computed, and also because they are needed for the computation of the sampling tolerance: otherwise unknown sampling biases may be present, and certainly the sampling tolerance will be unknowable, with the result that the reliability of the results cannot be determined objectively. The survey is then of the qualitative type which in some kinds of work will be the proper approach.

Now the chance of any particular household getting into the sample is meaningless unless certain rules of selection are followed faithfully. These rules require, among other things, *automatic selection* of the respondents, by which the final act of selection of the counties, cities, road-segments, blocks, households, or business establishments which are to be in the sample are drawn by rules that operate through the vagaries of chance. There is no other way to eliminate the bias of selection. The selection must not depend on expert judgment concerning the representativeness of any county or road-segment or household, or on the interviewer's judgment or convenience, or the desire of any particular people to be in or out of the sample, or to respond. Honesty, knowledge, and good intentions are not enough for the selection of a sample.

As for control of nonresponse (no one home who can answer the questions, refusal, failure to return a mailed questionnaire), a quantitative sampling plan must contain provision for eliciting information from that part of the universe which is not covered by the responses obtained through the mail or by the initial calls made by the interviewers. Without such provision the not-at-homes and refusals have no chance of getting into the sample. The cost of this part of the plan can be cut to its proper proportion by returning to only a subsample (perhaps 1 in 3 or 1 in 4) of the homes from which no answer was obtained at first call, and then weighting the results (by 3 or 4). An experienced inter-

viewer assigned to cover a subsample of 1 in 4 of the refusals may easily
report 50 to 80 per cent success, thus decreasing the refusal rate to a
half or a fifth of its initial value and enhancing the quality of the survey
to a point where it can be used with confidence.[2]

The bias of an estimating procedure may be zero or practically zero,
or it may be a type that introduces some appreciable percentage of
error. In a professional job of sampling, the bias so introduced is a
measurable quantity, and the estimating procedure is laid out in advance as part of the sampling plan which provides for measuring the
bias so introduced.

It is important not to confuse an estimating procedure with manipu-
lation such as weighting biased results by controlling segments of a
biased sample by adjusting them to known totals or proportions; cf. the
next section.

V

What has just been said regarding the control of biases and sampling
tolerance leads to some conclusions that are not always obvious and are
often overlooked. *First,* because the sampling tolerance is computable
and controllable in the quantitative sense only when the selection of
the households is automatic and removed from judgment, it follows that
formulas and charts intended for the calculation of sampling tolerance
are invalid and misleading unless proper rules of selection have been
followed. *Second,* even then, each sample-design or plan of procedure
has its own mathematical formula. A formula or chart applicable to one
design does not apply to another. For example, the formula for the
variance of samples of households selected at random from blocks which
have themselves been selected at random from strata each composed of
blocks of an equal number of households is very different from the
formula that would be used for selecting households at random directly
from the entire city.[3] If the blocks are drawn with probabilities propor-

[2] My colleague William N. Hurwitz has found a simple but important mathematical solution to the problem of what percentage of the nonrespondents of a questionnaire or initial call should be followed up by further interviews, in order to
obtain the greatest possible amount of information for a given total expenditure. The
important desideratum is the ratio of the cost of a mailed questionnaire to a personal
call, or the ratio of the initial call to the average cost of the additional calls necessary
to reduce the nonresponses to the required level. Mr. Hurwitz's solution was ex-
pounded March 15, 1943, at one of the Seminars in Sampling and Statistical Inference
at the Graduate School of the Department of Agriculture. It was later published in
the "Working Plan for the Annual Census of Lumber Produced in 1943," which is
obtainable from either the Census or the Forest Service. The results are being put to
use in government surveys, with consequent savings and increase in reliability.

[3] This is Eq. 3 in Hansen and Hurwitz' article, "On the Theory of Sampling from
Finite Populations," *Annals of Mathematical Statistics,* XIV (Dec. 1943) 333–62.

tional to size, one block per stratum, the formula is something else again.[4] No further evidence should be required as a protest against the sadly overworked npq formula, and charts based thereon, as a general-purpose formula; unfortunately no single formula exists, even for random sampling, and still less for the quota method or any biased procedure of selection.

If there is truth in this point, it follows that the important specification in a sample survey is *not how many interviews* but how these interviews were selected, and what was the final ratio of nonresponse. In other words, the important points in the specification of quality are not the number of interviews, but rather the width of the sampling tolerance and the steps taken to forestall biases.

Third, the development and even the use of formulas and charts for quantitative measures of sampling tolerance are professional problems in the province of mathematical statistics. Misinterpretations and mistakes may be expected when the underlying developments are misused. In particular, when biases of selection have been allowed to operate, as for instance in the quota method, no formula exists for the calculation of the sampling tolerance. Moreover, I might add, I question whether it would be possible to derive it: there would be the difficulty of reflecting, in the mathematics, the interviewers' preferences for certain classes of homes, affecting both bias and sampling tolerance. This assertion, let me repeat, is not uttered in condemnation of the quota method or any other method, but as a limitation that must be recognized in the interest of scientific advancement.

Fourth, a sampling procedure, whether qualitative or quantitative, cannot be credited (though it can be *dis*credited) by comparing its results with data from other sources. A procedure must be judged as well by its design—i.e., by the steps taken to control the biases of selection, estimation, and nonresponse. If it is to be a quantitative survey, it must be judged also by the expected standard error of the results. This is to say that although a procedure has been used over a period of years and has apparently always given good results, if no good reasons can be assigned for such performance and in particular if it is such that the sampling tolerance cannot be computed, it does not and never has satisfied the requirements of a quantitative method, in the sense that there never has been an objective prediction of what to expect in a future survey. The science of sampling has been set back many years by

---

[4] Cf. Eqs. 9 and 13 in the Hansen-Hurwitz article cited in the preceding footnote. Incidentally, in further support of the point made here, the formulas cited apply only when one sampling unit is drawn per stratum. The formulas proper for two or more sampling units have not yet been derived as of this writing.

too much faith in comparisons. Moreover, there is the question of efficiency: a procedure that is adequate may be over-adequate. Comparisons with census data do not answer the question: Is this plan the cheapest one that could have been devised to meet the requirements in reliability? As I remarked earlier, the statistician is singularly unimpressed by comparisons, and this is true of both qualitative and quantitative surveys.

Fifth, the practice of weighting results that have been elicited by biased methods is a dangerous practice.[5] This adjustment is often performed by using controls or weights, forcing certain marginal totals or proportions in the sample to agree with corresponding totals or proportions as determined by censuses of population, agriculture, business, or manufacturing. Unfortunately one never knows whether by weighting he is removing the bias of selection or making it worse. The difficulty does not lie in the fact that the census totals may be outdated and no longer accurate for adjustment: this is a problem indeed, but not the one that I am concerned with here. Weighting appropriately carried out will improve reliability, but in a quantitative survey it is permissible to weight only when the selection within strata is automatic.

VI

A few remarks should be made in regard to automatic selection. It is carried out by some mechanical or systematic procedure by which convenience and judgment are not permitted to influence the final selection of the counties, cities, road-segments, blocks, households, firms, or farms that constitute the sample. One kind of selection is called random within classes, and is equivalent to writing the addresses of all the households in a class on physically similar poker chips, one household to a chip, the chips thereupon being thoroughly shuffled and a sample of them (such as 100 of them, or 10 per cent of them) drawn blindfolded. A variant is a random selection of clusters of households, by which the addresses of several consecutive households might be written on one chip, and drawings made as before. Another way is to arrange the chips in some sort of order, thereupon to decimate them by drawing out every tenth one for the sample, using a random start. This is a so-called systematic selection. There are still other methods of drawing a sample by automatic selection, such as drawing elements with probability proportionate to size. An interesting random procedure which eliminates the bias of selection without detailed maps or lists has been developed by Alfred Politz, but there is no published reference to cite.

Automatic selection is easy to talk about, but not always easy to carry

---

[5] One of the earliest warnings against this practice was given by Corrado Gini and Luigi Galvani in the *Annali di Statistica* (Rome), Serie vi, vol. 4, 1929.

out. Some of the difficulties and dangers frequently met are contained in the following outline:

1. Quantitative sample-design, with control of costs and reliability, requires the services of a sampling expert. When such services are not obtainable, or are thought not to be worth the cost, recourse may be had to a complete coverage. Frequently, however, a plan of sampling is devised that depends on judgment-selection in one form or another, giving biases and sampling errors that cannot be computed.

2. Before automatic selection of households or areas is possible, it is necessary to acquire lists or maps showing the location and perhaps certain characteristics of the households or clusters of households that constitute the sampling units. These lists or maps may cost money, and their preparation and use must be directed by a sampling expert.

3. A household or area drawn into the sample by automatic selection may be difficult to reach, requiring an inconvenient trip across a city, or an uncomfortable and expensive journey into the country or over the mountains, perhaps in the cold and through mud.

4. Automatic selection requires call-backs, although efficient sample design will hold these to a minimum, as was mentioned. Substitution of one household for another is not permitted. It should be noted that no problem of call-backs is involved when, as in the quota method, an interviewer elicits information only from people who are at home.

The adoption of automatic selection, with the resulting elimination of biases and control of sampling variability, demands that difficulties of the kind just outlined be overcome in spite of their inconvenience. As for the expense, the net cost of the required reliability can be accurately computed because the reliability is under control and is a known function of the cost. If the desired reliability is deemed not worth the cost, two alternatives are open—abandon the survey, or accept wider sampling tolerances.

It would be decidedly incorrect to assume that in the use of automatic selection judgment is thrown to the wind and blind chance substituted. As a matter of fact, in modern sampling, judgment and all possible knowledge of the subject-matter under study are put to the best possible use. Knowledge and judgment come into play in many ways; for instance, *in defining the kind and size of sampling units,* in delineating homogeneous or heterogeneous areas, and in classifying the households into strata in ways that will be contributory toward reduction of sampling error. There is no limitation to the amount of judgment or knowledge of the subject that can be used, but this kind of knowledge is not allowed to influence the final selection of the particular cities, counties, blocks, roads, households, or business establishments that are to be in the sample; this final selection must be automatic, for it is only then that the bias of selection is eliminated and the sampling tolerance is measurable and controllable.

It would be equally incorrect to assume that biased methods of selection are being condemned. On the contrary, every effort should be put forth to make the fullest possible use of all kinds of cheap procedures of collection, such as the mailed questionnaire, but providing, *as an integral part of the plan,* a proper sample of that segment of the universe of households or business establishments not represented in the biased response. In this way the biases are evaluated and subtracted out, and the reliability of the total is ensured. Hurwitz' plan (cited earlier) for obtaining an unbiased result at the lowest cost by eliciting responses from only a proper subsample of people initially not at home or refusing to give information is a special case of a more general approach which could be fruitfully exploited on a larger scale.[6]

VII

There are certain aspects of sampling that are important from the standpoint of cost, particularly when the cost comes out of public funds. If the survey is one in which the data are to be used in arriving at some critical decision involving the health, security, or property of some segment of the population, it may be very important that the reliability be measurable. The ability to compute objectively the reliability of results is, therefore, in most government surveys, held to be of vital importance. One of the most important developments in modern sampling procedures is that the plan of procedure furnishes the measure of reliability of the data obtained or to be obtained—i.e., the plan furnishes a measure of the sampling tolerance (such as 3 per cent, 5 per cent, 10 or 25 per cent), and also assures control of the biases of selection, estimation, and nonresponse. Thus, through proper planning, statistics can be bought on a quality-for-cost basis—so much quality (sampling tolerance) at a certain cost, and a specified reduction in sampling tolerance obtainable at so much additional cost.

On the other hand, if a sample consists wholly of "typical" elements (areas, road-segments, blocks, households, firms, or farms) whose selection depends on expert judgment, or the judgment of the interviewer, or the willingness of people to respond, then there are no known rules

[6] Another example occurs in Morris H. Hansen's testimony before the Federal Communications Commission on April 15, 1946, transcripts of which are obtainable from Ward and Paul, 1760 Pennsylvania Avenue, Washington 6. Docket 6741. Still another example is furnished by *The Enumerative-Check Census* by Calvert L. Dedrick and Morris H. Hansen, being vol. iv of the *Census of Partial Employment, Unemployment, and Occupations: 1937.*

for calculating the reliability of the results. The reliability must then be judged subjectively instead of being furnished objectively by the sample itself. This introduces no difficulty unless the subjective judgments are at odds, in which case the reliability of the results of a survey, and hence their usefulness also, are unknown quantities and the survey is a questionable purchase.

In quantitative studies the problem in sample-design is no longer "to get results just as good as we can get them." Such a statement is devoid of meaning, however good the intentions behind it. Rather, the problem is first to decide what reliability is required, and then to design a sampling procedure that will just meet it at the lowest possible cost, and to know how greatly the cost will be increased if greater reliability is demanded. Framed in another way, the problem is to design a survey that will yield the most information possible for a given allowable cost. Either way, there is implied an aspect of sampling that needs to be expressly stated and emphasized, namely this: *it is impossible to compare the costs of two proposed methods of conducting a survey unless the reliability or amount of information to be obtained from each of them is known and controllable in the plans.* When the procedure is such that the main biases are not removed, and the sampling tolerance is neither computable nor controllable, there is no way of saying whether the survey is cheap enough or too costly, because its quality is unknown. It is not sufficient that a procedure *might* give good results. A survey producing results of unknown and unknowable quality is not a wise purchase, particularly if public funds are involved.

THE CONSUMER AND HIS INTERESTS
By
C. WEST CHURCHMAN

THERE are few terms in our language so puzzling in their usage as the term "consumer." The consumer is everybody, his interests are everyone's. And yet few can say what makes any one of us a consumer, and fewer still can tell us how to measure his interests. The consumer is the little man who is everywhere.

This does not deny that within certain fields it is easy enough to determine who the consumer is, and even to evaluate his best interests. The producer of soap, or writing paper, or fountain pens can develop a fairly clear picture of his consumer if he conducts a well-designed sampling survey of the population, and by the right sort of questionnaire he may even be able to formulate some definite ideas as to kind of article that will best serve his consumer.

But there are some of us who like to step back a bit from particular fields of manufacture, and attempt to study the consumer-at-large. We should like to be able to find certain general principles descriptive of the consumer and the best techniques of satisfying his wants. Such an attempt, for example, has been made by the National and the Social Science Research Councils, which have recently established a joint committee to study the measurement of opinion, attitudes, and consumer wants. Again, the American Society for Testing Materials (ASTM) has founded a committee to consider specifications for ultimate consumer goods. Both of these committees, together with many groups similarly organized, are attempting to discover the basic ways of studying the consumer to the end of best satisfying his needs.

And all such studies, if their methodology is to be scientific in approach, must begin by trying to say who the consumer is, and what are his interests.

Thus phrased, the problem becomes one of general methodology, and the attempt will be made here to apply some of the basic principles of experimental methodology to the determination of an adequate definition of the consumer and his interests.

Let us begin with a few "common sense" definitions, so that we can have a basis for discussion. The enlarged *Century Dictionary* defines a consumer as "one who destroys the exchangeable value of a commodity by using it: the opposite of a producer." We shall not have much quarrel with the second part of this definition; consumer and producer are evidently correlatives: he who does not produce, consumes. But the first part the *Century's* definition contains a fundamental weakness. By its account, the user of a 1941 Ford car has not been a consumer during the past few years, at least on the Black Market, since the "exchangeable value" has certainly not been destroyed. For this reason it would be preferable not to define the consumer and his interests in terms of price scales, lest an inflation among certain commodities make producers of us all. Let us try instead a modification of the dictionary definition, as follows: *"The consumer is one who utilizes an instrument of production in such a way that it becomes less efficient with respect to its future uses."*

Now some of the more cautious may feel that the consumer has still eluded us. Is the reader of a book a consumer, and if so, are we trying to say that the book is less useful, once it has been read? And even though we may talk of the destruction of place utility by the book readers, what of the student in a school or college? Is the process of being educated a process of consumption? If so, should we talk about utility-destruction in connection with the general consumer? Again, isn't the industry that uses machines to manufacture goods a consumer, and doesn't such an industry increase utility?

The ASTM's administrative committee on ultimate consumers' goods has made a suggestion on the last point; they have defined the ultimate consumer goods to be *"materials or products which, in the 'as is' condition are intended for sale to an individual purchaser for his personal property or use, and not for fabrication or resale."*

The ASTM definition has succeeded in avoiding any reference to utility-destruction in its definition, but because of the particular aims of the committee, it has introduced a commercial emphasis in its reference to sale. From the very general viewpoint here, we don't want the definition of consumer to depend upon a certain basis of exchange. We want rather a definition that will hold good regardless of the particular manner in which things are bought and sold, indeed, independent of whether things are ever bought at all. A consumer must be a consumer whether he belongs to a primitive society, a capitalist society, or a socialist society, and presumably his interests are just the same, whether or not he buys his articles.

In order to make an end to this sort of Socratic dialectic, which can be extended *ad nauseam,* let us turn to the general methodologist for some advice in matters of defining of this sort. Modern methodology, through a long and tedious experience with problems just like the one we have been considering, has come out with the following useful principle, which we shall apply to the consumer-problem: *"All definitions of universal characteristics of human behavior should be defined in terms of the purpose of such behavior."*

It would take us well beyond the scope of this paper to define in specific terms what the methodologist means by the term "purpose," but an example or so will assist in clarifying the point of his principle. No one would attempt to define the term "vehicle" in terms of structure alone (e.g., in terms of wheels attached to a body) because for every such structural definition it is possible to find a counter-example which fails to comply with the requirements of the definition but which everyone recognizes to be a vehicle (e.g., for the example already given, a toboggan). The result is that sound methodology requires, in the defining of terms like "vehicle," a common characteristic which is independent of any particular structural attribute; in this case, the common property is "potential producer of a change in locale." This common property we call a functional property. In the same way, it would be foolish to define the act of creating a great work of art in terms of some specific technique; the schools of great art come and go, but for all this change we still recognize the products of the modern artist as great; hence the proper defining of the production of great art must be independent of any specific behavior patterns on the part of the artist. Whatever may be the common characteristic which describes such creation, we say that it is a purposive property. Hence, the methodologist's principle may be rephrased as follows: *"All definitions of universal characteristics of human behavior should be defined in terms of a common property of a class of behavior patterns, the common property being independent of any structural aspect of the behavior."*

In the light of this principle, the problem we have set ourselves becomes: *"What is the characteristic of all activities which are common to consumption of produced goods?"*

Before proceeding to answer this question, we must make use of a second principle the methodologist has developed. This principle is a precaution to the definition-seeker, and helps us to emphasize the basic property of purposive activity. The principle is: *"The purpose of an individual is merely the predominant trait in his behavior patterns; there will be cases, and, indeed, there may be many of them, where he fails to attain his goal."*

This principle tells us that in our search for the consumer purpose, we should not expect to find that everyone we call a consumer has succeeded in his ends. For an individual to exhibit a purpose, we have said that one must be able to find a common property among the many activities which he exhibits. But this common property does not necessarily imply success in his purposes, for then purposive activity would be far rarer than we usually recognize it to be. Rather, the common property is one of potential success, the potentiality being measured by certain operationally defined characteristics of behavior in general.

One final word from the methodologist, to avoid the pitfalls of a loose or metaphysical kind of definition: *"The purpose defined must be one that can be determined by the methods of experimental science."*

This means that whatever may be our definition of the consumer, it should be at least theoretically possible to determine whether an individual, or group of individuals, are to be considered as consumers, on the basis of experimental tests on their behavior (attitudes, actions, etc.).

Now the defining of a consumer in accordance with these fundamental principles of methodology, will be facilitated by first defining the correlative term "producer," because the producer's purposes are much more clearly delineated, at least within our present-day society. The following offering, I think, will not be open to too much objection on the part of the most frequent users of the term: *"An individual is said to be a producer of an object X if his purpose is to create X in such a way that it will be useful to at least some persons in the accomplishment of their goals."*

This definition appears to satisfy all the methodological requirements we have set down, with the possible exception of the last, for we must state what "useful" means if we expect to conduct precise experimental tests. But this problem presents no very great difficulty, since the term "utility" has been studied so widely within the various social sciences. Probably the briefest and most precise definition of the "useful" would be the following: *"An instrument is said to be 'useful' if it can become an aspect of an individual's behavior in such a way that the behavior is more efficient in the accomplishment of an end."*

Now if this definition adequately characterizes the producer, then our search for the consumer has ended, since:

"An individual is said to be a 'consumer' of an object of production X, if he employs it for a purpose different from the purpose of production."

In other words, the consumer is anyone who uses the results of productive activity for ends which are not productive in their purpose. This definition has avoided any mention of methods of barter and exchange; it has avoided the necessity of talking about "intention to sell." A consumer may certainly intend to sell an object he has bought; most of us intend to sell the cars we buy, and yet as long as we are using the cars for nonproductive purposes, we are consumers. The definition has also avoided any reference to the ultimate consumer. The man who makes a cupping-machine is a producer, and he who makes cups with it is a producer, but not with respect to the same object. Thus "consumption" and "production" are terms which are relative to certain objects and to the intentions or purposes of an individual with respect to these objects.

It might be thought that if we can claim success in trapping the consumer within the tyranny of our words, we have almost automatically caught hold of the meaning of his interests as well. For don't interests refer to purposes, and haven't we already defined the consumer in terms of his purposes? Shall we say that an action serves the interest of the consumer if it assists him in the accomplishment of his consumer-ends? Shall we equate consumer interest with consumer desire? So that, if we want to know whether a certain manufactured article serves the consumer interest, we need only measure preferences, evaluate biological factors such as health, well-being, etc., and in general run the entire gamut of people's desires. What could be simpler? Or, at least, what could be simpler to state, since, as this Conference shows, the actual measurement of these things requires all the ingenuity and experience the biologist, psychologist, and sociologist can bring to bear.

And yet, even if we could say that all the problems of health-measurement and preference-measurement were completely solved, could we then assert that we had completely solved the problem of measuring the consumer's interests? We take one of the most serious fallacies of the consumer problem to be the assumption that the measurement of consumer interest depends solely upon the measurement of consumer desire.

In the first place, the consumer turns out to be a very complicated and unpleasant sort of fellow. He insists on preferring things that are not good for him. An intensive advertising campaign can make the consumer long for articles that either don't satisfy his basic needs, or are detrimental to them. Sometimes the desires of one consumer, or group of consumers, are in direct conflict with the desires of others. Hence, if we expect to satisfy consumer interests in this sense of interests, we shall have to effect a repeal of the laws of logic, so that we can do two contradictory things at the same time. Even worse, a single consumer desires things that are in conflict: he likes strong tobacco and strong liquor; he also likes to live long and well. How can we best serve his interests?

The obvious reply to all this is one that is going to get us into some more trouble. We should like to say that only those consumer purposes which serve his best ends can be used in considering consumer interest. I say that this suggestion is going to get us into some trouble, because the economist and the sociologist are constantly warning us against the danger of introducing value judgments into the field of science. "Leave ethics to the philosophers," they say. "We've got enough problems of our own trying to find the basic sociological facts and laws, without bothering about what is 'good' and 'bad' in some ultimate philosophical sense." And this is a good warning, for the philosophers have been all too prone to keep their results out of the hands of the experimental scientist, who consequently has no inclination to work in typically philosophical fields.

And yet the scientist has begun to realize more and more of late that he cannot escape the basic ethical problems that are becoming so pressing in our culture. We don't ask whether it is a fact that atomic energy is available to industry, that the OPA is continuing, etc. We ask rather, should the secret of the atom be released, should the OPA be continued. We raise issues of value, whether we like to or not.

The realization that a science of value is badly needed has recently come about in a very strange field for this sort of thing, industrial engineering. The progressive industrial engineer has been developing techniques of quality control of the final product to such a precise extent that he can tell the manufacturer exactly what are his risks if he employs a given method of inspection. For example, if the inspection plan is based on attributes, he can tell the manufacturer how frequently he will pass lots having a certain percentage of defective articles. The use of the statistical measure "average outgoing quality level," which is derived from these quality-control procedures, is now practically standard in many industries. Its use was one of the outstanding contributions of industrial engineering to the war-effort. In terms of these precisely defined quality-control concepts, we are also able to define the producer's risk and the consumer's risk, as a basis for evaluating a given inspection scheme.

And yet all these precise statistical measures are not worth their weight in paper until we have also employed other measures, measures which depend upon a science of value for their precise defining. What good does it do us to know the average outgoing-quality level unless we also know how serious a defective article will be for the consumer? A defective telephone will not be nearly as bad as a defective drug, let us say. And yet what does "bad" mean here?

As Dr. Deming has put it on other occasions, the result of an inspection procedure is always the basis for a future action. To evaluate the procedure, therefore, we must be able to evaluate the efficiency of this action with respect to our best interests. It does no good, and a great deal of harm, to set up elaborate quality-control procedures based upon highly developed techniques of mathematical statistics, if we do not at the same time make a very careful study of the general consequences of these procedures.

It follows that the determination of the risk or probability of making a wrong decision is not enough; one must also be able to measure in some sense the importance of his mistake.[1] The method that the army used at the beginning of the war to inspect detonator caps did guarantee a rather high average outgoing-quality level, but the loss incurred by a failing cap might be tremendous, so that relative to this loss, the army's techniques were bad.

The moral of all this is now clear. However distasteful the task, the social scientist who wishes to measure consumer interest must first make certain basic presuppositions about value; he must decide what purposes should be satisfied, and what purposes should not.

To this end, we may again turn to the general methodologist, who in recent years has been attempting to formulate clearly the basic principles of the science of ethics in such a way that these principles can be employed fruitfully by the experimental scientist. We shall make the discoveries of the methodologist the closing theme of this paper. These

[1] The measure we are interested in here is closely allied with the "weight function" introduced by Wald into statistical theory; see A. Wald, "Principles of Statistical Inference" (Notre Dame, 1941).

remarks of course will have a very general character, but within the framework of a paper of this sort we can only phrase the basic conditions necessary for measuring interests; it will be up to a progressive social science to discover techniques for applying these measures.

As a beginning, we may employ the first principle of the methodologist which we have already stated: however "human value" is defined, it must be defined in terms of the purposes of individuals. That is, the "valuable" will be whatever serves some specific purpose. The fundamental task of a science of ethics is to specify that purpose which distinguishes a good act from a bad one. We shall also want to make use of the methodologist's third principle: however this basic purpose is defined, one must be able to determine by experimental methods whether or not a given course of action is an adequate means to the ethical end. Thus we should be able to measure ethical efficiency as precisely at least as we can measure the efficiency of a machine in the manufacture of a certain item.

The empirical situation can be described as follows: an article is made available to an individual who intends to use it for a certain purpose, a nonproductive purpose. We are now interested in measuring how a consumer's interest will be served if he follows out his intentions. For example, a certain kind of tooth paste is put on the market; in evaluating the product with respect to the consumer interest we should like to know the possible losses he would incur in using this tooth paste rather than any other in washing his teeth.

One aspect of interest we have already mentioned: we have said that the consumers' purposes are apt to conflict, and that if they do conflict, then in some sense there will be a loss in interest if one of these purposes is pursued. This suggests that the measure of interest will have to depend in its initial formulation upon a specific purpose.

We picture a given class of consumers as having a number of purposes; some of these purposes will be satisfied if an article is used, and some will not. In many cases, some of the consumer purposes may actually fail: for example, drinking a poor coffee, while it satisfies the purpose of stimulation, may be detrimental to the purpose of good health.

We may therefore talk about the legitimacy of a consumer purpose in fairly precise experimental language. Associated with any given purpose of the consumer-group, there will be the probability of the purpose's being fulfilled if the article X is used in a certain manner.

In more general terms, the use of X will increase the chances of the attainment of certain consumer goals, but will not have any effect at all on the chances of attaining other goals. This suggests the following definition of the legitimacy of a consumer good: *"The measure of the legitimacy of a consumer good X with respect to a specific purpose, or goal, Y, is the difference in the probability of attaining Y if X is used, and the probability of attaining Y if the most efficient known means for the consumer is used."*

The length of this definition warrants an example. A manufacturer places on the market a certain soap which sells for the same price as any other brand. The goal Y in this case may be the cleansing of clothes to a certain degree of purity from inorganic or organic matter within a certain time, the degree of purity being measurable by laboratory tests. Then we may determine, for a specified amount of the soap, the probability that the desired degree of cleanliness is attained. The difference between this probability for the new soap, and the probability for the best soap that science knows how to make, will be a measure of the legitimacy of the new soap.[2] If the new soap turns out to be better than any other on the market for its price, then its legitimacy measure will be positive; if it turns out to be neither better nor worse than some other brand, its legitimacy measure will be zero; and if it turns out to be worse than the best available brand, the measure will be negative. We have included a price-stipulation in this test, to simplify the example. To compare the legitimacy of an article relative to others of its type over the whole price scale, a more general definition of the consumer purpose than the purely economic one would have to be given.

Now the measure of the legitimacy of a consumer good is relative not only to the other available means, but also to a specific purpose. Relative to some purposes, the article may have a high legitimacy value: a certain brand of whiskey may provide the best way to become pleasantly drunk. But relative to other goals, the legitimacy value may be very low: the whiskey is certainly not the best means, at its price, of attaining longevity. To generalize upon the concepts of legitimacy, so that we can evaluate an article with respect to all the consumer-purposes, we should have first to make a classification of the predominant consumer-purposes of a group, and in terms of these basic purposes derive a list of weighted legitimacy measures, the average (or some other statistic) of which could then be taken as the general legitimacy measure of the article.

The manner in which the weights may be assigned to the various purposes of individuals and groups may now be discussed briefly. As a rather obvious beginning, let us suggest that the importance of a purpose is relative to its generality; one purpose is more general than an-

---

2 The goal Y in this case is specified by a time interval (and perhaps also by the kind of water and temperature of the water used). It may be possible in many cases to specify more general purposes and find more general measures of efficiency.

other, if success in its attainment implies success in the attainment of the other, and more besides. Thus the purpose of good health is a more general one than the purpose of eating a nourishing meal. From this we might immediately infer that the most valuable purpose would be the most general purpose of all: that purpose which will enable us to obtain any end whatsoever. Besides the element of contradiction contained in such a generalized purpose, there are other objections to its use as a criterion of weighting less general purposes. For one thing, we wish to have no sympathy with a program aimed to simplify our desires, or eliminate them; one of the most insidious types of social exploitation occurs when the preferences of a group are perverted and simplified, so that actually the members of the exploited group desire very little, or desire objects their exploiters can cheaply and profitably supply. We could hardly assign a very high legitimacy score to the purpose of an exploiter who was trying to pervert the group desires in this manner, even though he is actually working to satisfy any existent end of the group. In the same manner, we must assign a low legitimacy to an advertising campaign designed to make the consumer give up one desire for a desire the producer can profitably satisfy, when in some sense we think the new desire to be less worth while.

Admitting as inadequate this simple definition of a most general purpose (one satisfying any desire), we must proceed to a further refinement. To make a long and complicated story a short and oversimplified one, we suppose that it is possible by an examination of the history of societies with respect to their aims to determine predominant purposes expressive of the aims of man, not as viewed from one age or social group, but as viewed throughout all the changes of societies in their various historical aspects. Such predominant purposes let us call "historical." Let us then define the most general purpose to be the satisfaction of any given historical purpose. Examples of such historical purposes would evidently be health, comfort, longevity, well-being, etc., though to effect the aims of this discussion these purposes would all have to be made experimentally explicit. We then argue that the weight attached to any given purpose, be it of individual or group, depends on the efficiency of this purpose with respect to the predominant historical purposes, i.e., with respect to the general end of satisfying the aims of mankind as exemplified in history. The program we are proposing is a large one: it entails setting up a science of history adequate to the discovery of these predominant purposes, and a method of evaluating specific ends in terms of their efficiency with respect to the general end. Although crude beginnings of legitimacy scores could even now be effective within social science, it will be clear that the future success of the proposed program depends upon our attitude regarding the future of methods within the social sciences. If we argue that we can never attain experimental controls in this domain, then we shall have to admit in the same breath that we can never hope to evaluate social aims, e.g., never evaluate consumer interests. For one who wishes to generalize on these matters, to give up the hope of experimental control in social and historical research is tantamount to giving up the hope of any science, any experiment, any control at all; for is not science itself a consumer service, and does not every science have to be evaluated with respect to its aims and its methods?

SPECIFICATIONS FOR CONSUMERS' GOODS

PARTICIPANTS

CHAIRMAN: A. G. Ashcroft, *Alexander Smith and Sons.*
SPEAKERS: S. S. Wilks, *Department of Mathematics, Princeton University;* Paul Peach, *Institute of Statistics, University of North Carolina;* Ralph F. Breyer, *Department of Marketing and Foreign Commerce, University of Pennsylvania;* J. H. Curtiss, *Assistant to the Director, Bureau of Standards;* D. H. Palmer, *Hospital Bureau of Standards and Supplies.* DISCUSSION: Milton Rubin, *A. J. Wood and Co.;* Wilbur Phillips, *Social Unit Institute, Inc.;* Paula Strobach, *University of Pennsylvania.*

ASHCROFT: I am going to break what I thought was an excellent precedent by previous Panel Chairmen, and that was for him to say very little, because I think this particular phase of the Conference requires some orientation, or else we may get into areas of discussion later on which are not so pertinent as we had perhaps hoped. I think that Prof. Churchman's remarks last night and this morning, and Prof. E. A. Singer's paper set the keynote for this Conference, and it is one, I am sure, with which all the discussers in today's panel will agree: that the scientists in general have given up the hope that one man, or single group, can answer the problems of consumer goods specifications. It requires a combination of the sciences: of economics, marketing, sociology, etc. The recognition of this is indicated by such conferences as this, and of new areas of coöperation in various technical societies. I recall a paper by Roland P. Soole three years ago, in which he made the same suggestions with regard to the development of research in industry; that one could practically orient the growth of the various fields of applied sciences in industry to eras of about twenty years. For example, 1860 to 1880 was an era of civil engineering, with its growth of railroads and canals; 1880–1900, the era of electrical developments; and 1900–1920 the era of mechanical engineering, the development of mechanical and production industries, the airplane, the automobile, and power in general. 1920–1940 was the era of chemical engineering. And the question is asked "What of 1940 to 1946?" The answer is that it will be known as the era of combination of the sciences for the betterment of human wants in the fabricating industries particularly—the industries with which the consumers are primarily concerned. I might outline some of the things that have occurred for those of you who are not in the applied industries. An advisory committee of the American Standards Association on Ultimate Consumer Goods has been in existence for two years with a membership of thirty-five or forty people, representing all types of consumer and technical societies.

Recently there was correspondence between Secretary Wallace and Charles E. Wilson on the general subject of the position of the Government, particularly in the development of consumer goods specifications. The American Society for Testing Materials has been more active during the last two or three years in this field. An administrative committee of the society was set up to orient the standard committees on the subject of ultimate consumer goods. Dr. Churchman read a definition that this ASTM group had developed, a definition of ultimate consumer goods, and made pertinent criticisms. It is important, of course, that we should agree on some definition, and the one tentatively proposed may not be final. I think we should also define, the meaning of the term "Specifications for Consumer Goods," the title of our panel. Can we agree at least to emphasize only one of the four different types of specifications which might be assumed to be included? I don't think we want to include a type of minimum specification as an adjunct to price factors, for that is in the era of economics and politics. It is a need and an asset in that era, but it is a methodological picture in the field of politics and economics, rather than a science. Nor do we, I think, wish to include in specifications for consumer goods those specifications intended to identify, that is definitely define more clearly, the properties of materials or products for the purchaser of goods in mass production lots. Such a purchaser wants a specific product of his own; he identifies it properly so that he gets what he wants for resale; but he is not an ultimate consumer. Nor do we want to include specifications for acceptance requirements, aimed at defining for the purchaser of goods in lots whether or not these goods are what he has specified. What we are interested in is the specifications for the methods of testing and identifying consumer values and wants, singly or in combination.

I am going to ask PROFESSOR S. S. WILKS if he will now start the discussion . . . . .

RESEARCH ON CONSUMER PRODUCTS AS A COUNTERPART OF WARTIME RESEARCH

WILKS: First of all, I should like to say that I am not an expert at all in the field of consumer research. My interest lies in possibilities of statistical methods in the field. It seems to me that this whole field of consumer research has an extremely large ingredient of social science problems.

I should like first to make a few comments on a type of activity that was carried on during the war, under such headings as *operational analysis* and *operational research*. There is a similarity between this type of war-time activity and the activity that is being carried out in the field of consumer research which is worth pointing out.

As an example of an operational research group, let me take one I know something about: the Navy Operational Research Group, which was established in 1942 in Boston in connection with anti-submarine warfare operations. After functioning there for several months, with a very small staff of personnel, the Group was set up in Washington at a good safe distance of two blocks from the Navy Building. There was a considerable amount of skepticism on the part of naval officers as to what such a group of academic scientists could do for the war effort, but very soon some results on search tactics were obtained by this Group which were very useful in dealing with the German submarine menace in the summer of 1942, and shortly after the Group was moved into the Navy Building. After that the Group grew rapidly, won the confidence of the military, and was soon attached to the Office of the Commander-in-Chief of the United States Fleet.

The Group did a great deal of work, not only within the boundaries of this country but overseas. Appreciation of the effectiveness of operational research grew constantly during the war, and by the end of it these operational research groups, both British and American, were set up in command headquarters in various parts of the world. These operational research groups consisted of mixed teams. They had engineers, physicists, chemists, psychologists, mathematicians, statisticians, and various other professional men attached to them. Their job was to study the effectiveness of the operation of men and equipment under combat conditions, and to evaluate tactics. During the war the industrial power of this country and England was geared to the training of men and the production of war material. These groups studied the effectiveness of these products for the purpose for which they were designed, by going to the theatre of operations and working with the users of the products—the men in combat. They reported their findings to the theatre commanders and back through channels to their headquarters in this country and England, and in many instances these reports were effective in improving equipment, training, and tactics.

Now let us examine the analogy between war-time operational research and peace-time consumer research. In peace time we have a huge segment of our economy geared to manufacturing consumer products. So we have here the problem of studying the effectiveness with which the peace-time consumer products, such as refrigerators, automobiles, and electric appliances, are doing the job that they are supposed to do, and we are evaluating this effectiveness by going to the users of the products—the ultimate consumers. This consumer research work has been going on after a fashion for a long time, but now there seems to be a movement in the direction of greatly increased activity which is growing by leaps and bounds. The demands which are being placed on the various groups and market research organizations to do consumer research surveys are heavy.

The urgency with which this consumer research work is being carried out is, in many cases, outrunning the basic research that is needed to provide a genuine scientific basis for the work. If one looks into the problems which exist in this field, one finds two general categories of problems: one of them is that of reaching a sample of people appropriate for any given consumer research study, and the other is that of reliably eliciting information from such people once they are reached. In other words, the first category of problems for making consumer surveys is the sampling problem, and the second one that of interviewing. The problems of interviewing seem to be much greater and more complicated than those of sampling. Everyone in the field of market research, polling, and government surveys recognizes the existence of a vast unexplored territory of interviewing methodology. They know that the slightest change in the wording of questions often leads to unexpectedly large variations in response distributions. It therefore seems that one of the most important things needed in the field of consumer research is a basic and systematic fund of information relating to interviewing methodology, which would be available to everyone interested in the field. What is apparently happening is that information of this type is being accumulated at various places, but it has never been brought together into a fund of basic scientific knowledge. The same is true to a much lesser extent with regard to information relating to sampling methodology. In order to build interviewing and sampling methodology into anything resembling a science, a great deal of basic information must be brought together to show how well various interviewing and sampling procedures operate, and how they compare with each other. This will take a long time, but it can be speeded by coöperation which I shall describe presently. But the point to make here is that in order for these fields to become scientific it is necessary to have a broad fund of basic information. It is through such funds of systematic information that astronomy, biology, chemistry, and physics have grown into sciences. Social science stands challenged to build up such funds of knowledge. This point has been driven home in all the discussions of the place of social science in the national science legislation program. It has been crystallized into the compromise Kilgore-Magnuson bill S.1850 in the following words:

The functions of each division shall be prescribed by the Administrator after receiving the advice of the Board, except that until the Administrator and the Board have received general recommendations from the Division of Social Science regarding the support of social science research, it shall be limited to studies of the impact of scientific discovery on the general welfare and studies required in connection with other projects supported by the foundation.

Now under what conditions can research and accumulation of facts in the fields of sampling and interviewing be speeded up and put on a scale commensurate with the practical demands being placed on this field of activity? It seems to me that this can be done only through a great deal of coöperation among business organizations, government agencies, and universities. If one looks back into the history of the physical sciences, one finds that a great amount of the basic fund of basic knowledge and facts have come out of university laboratories, which have been sufficient to deal with many of the physical science problems. But such problems as that of finding how well an interviewing system works or a sampling method works cannot be done in a university laboratory. The study of such problems is a costly undertaking and can be done only by business organizations or government agencies set up especially for the purpose. What we need to do is to devise ways for speeding up gathering of this information, and provide for the comparison of various methods of interviewing, and of various methods of sampling.

There is quite a lot of discussion now as to whether this method of sampling or interviewing is better than that one, but it seems to me that the only effective way to proceed is to make provision for the comparison of the various methods under as highly controlled a set of conditions as possible. These comparisons cannot be made by one organization, or one government agency. They require the coöperation of many agencies and organizations in order to get the basic information that is needed, each agency or organization contributing what it can in the course of its work to overall plans for getting comparative information. University personnel can help in such activity by critical appraisal and by planning the collection of basic data and analyzing and interpreting it.

A step was taken in 1945 by the National Research Council and the Social Science Research Council which looks promising in the matter of coöperation. These two councils set up a joint committee of experts in polling, psychology, sociology, and statistics, for the purpose of stimulating research in sampling and interviewing procedures, with the hope of being able to obtain coöperation among the various organizations and agencies so as to get the type of data needed in studying the effectiveness of various interviewing and sampling methods. We need to have a lot of basic information on how effective panels of respondents are for various purposes. They are important and are widely used, but where is the pool of basic information on panels? There are all kinds of questions that come up in the use of panels, such as conditioning of respondents by repeated interviewing, maintenance of a panel, etc. A fund of facts is needed on these questions. It is hoped that the joint committee of the National Research Council and Social Science Research Council to which I referred will be effective in helping to bring about the coöperation needed in order to obtain such information.

ASHCROFT: PROFESSOR PAUL PEACH is going to discuss . . . . .

LABORATORY TESTING AND ACTUAL QUALITY IN THE CONSUMER GOODS FIELD

PEACH: The problems involved in specifications for consumer goods have at least four aspects:

1. What does the consumer want or need?
2. How can this need be described in definite operational terms?
3. How can we tell whether a particular specimen fills the need?
4. What will be the consequences of supplying this need?

No one professional group can furnish adequate answers to these questions; the task calls for coöperation among engineers, chemists, physicists, psychologists, economists, sociologists, logicians, and lawyers, as well as specialists in education, government, management, and marketing; these groups must have in common at least some basic philosophical viewpoints, so that they can agree on fundamental objectives; and their inquiries must recognize the fundamental unity of all science which modern specialization has tended to obscure. To demonstrate the ramified nature of the subject we need only discuss the four aspects of consumer specifications.

A specification is a description of what is wanted. This definition is glib; but it rarely happens that the consumer has any very clear notion of what he wants or needs. Consider for example cigarettes, say Camels, Chesterfields, and Lucky Strikes. It remains to be proved that they can be told apart by any method short of reading the label or something equivalent. Nevertheless people do have strong preferences, physical or psychological. Ask any smoker why he prefers A rather than B or C; he will reply in general terms—B is too strong; C irritates his throat. But suppose now that the manufacturers of B and C ask the A smoker for more definite information, with a view to changing the quality of B and C to make them better than A. They will not get it; whatever may be the basis for the smoker's preferring A, he (and other A smokers) cannot give definite enough information about it to support management action.

As often as not, manufacturers themselves have no clear idea of what their product is or ought to be. For illustration, we may consider shoes, say men's oxfords. They range in price from about $3.00 to $15.00 a pair for mass production brands. Last fall I got into the shoe industry for a little while and I asked three men who were responsible executives in the shoe business—men of large experience who presumably knew something about the field—what was the difference between a $5.00 shoe and a $13.50 shoe: I got three different answers. One was, "There isn't any consistent difference; the man who buys a $13.50 shoe will get longer wear out of it than the man who buys a $5.00 shoe because the man who buys the expensive shoe spends most of his time with his feet under a desk; otherwise he is riding in a car. The man who can afford the $5.00 shoe has to work harder and wears them out quicker."

That was one answer. The second man who, as far as I could make out, was equally capable of giving authoritative answers said, "There is a quality difference, it is inherent in the material and workmanship. In the $13.50 shoe you are more fussy about discarding leather that doesn't quite measure up to the standards. You pay your people more, so you get a better all-round shoe, and naturally it wears better."

The third man said, "There is a real quality difference between the shoes; it is not, however, inherent in the materials. There is only one thing out of which most shoes are made, and that is leather. It is true that there are different grades of leather, but generally speaking the whole shoe industry uses the same general type, with the exception of a few shoes that go out in the extreme low-price field. Where the difference comes in is in the fact that in the expensive shoes more time is given to the building of the shoe. When it is placed on the wooden form or last over which it is built, it remains there for a week or ten days, during which time the leather accommodates itself to the particular shape that it is supposed to have, and by the time the last is pulled out of the shoe and the shoe is put into the box it has adjusted itself to the final shape. The cheap shoe has got to be produced on pressure of time, so that when it reaches the consumer it is still in what you might call green condition."

Now it may very well be true that by many standards the $15.00 shoe is better than the $5.00 shoe; whether it is better than three $5.00 shoes is uncertain. It is also uncertain whether the standards by which the $15.00 shoe is better are the right standards—whether, in fact, the $5.00 shoe might not be better by standards at least equally valid. What is not in the least uncertain is that if the Government should offer shoe manufacturers a subsidy of 50¢ per pair on the condition that the money should be used to build 50¢ worth of quality into each pair, no shoe manufacturer anywhere would know how to use the money. Even given a standard for judging shoes, he could still not do it; the shoe industry does not have a quantitative engineering knowledge of its product.

Such knowledge cannot be obtained without a scientific inquiry on a very broad basis, and no one group exists which, unaided, could plan and carry out the research. The experience and knowledge of manufacturers of shoes and shoe machinery would have to be augmented by contributions from specialists in leather and textiles, from large buyers of shoes (such as the army and Sears Roebuck), from podiatrists and style experts, and doubtless from others whose connection with shoes is not recognized now. The experiment would have to be designed and conducted and the results analyzed by the best statisticians, and probably with the coöperation of some agency such as the post office. Finally, the findings would have to be reviewed by the groups already mentioned. The whole project would call for a pooling of knowledge on a scale hitherto unknown even in the great coöperative researches of the war.

It is quite easy to see that equally broad needs arise in connection with the other three aspects of specifications previously mentioned. To describe a need in definite operational terms we must bridge a language gap. The consumer needs or wants something, say a watch that keeps good time. But the watchmaker thinks in terms of hairsprings, compensated balance wheels, jewels, and pinions—in a technical jargon that is quite unintelligible to the watch-user. Someone must act as interpreter between these two groups, to tell the watchmaker, in watchmaker's language, what the consumer wants. Back of him are the physicist and the expert on testing materials, who try to ascertain causal relationships. Unless these relationships are known in a quantitative way, economy will suffer from the inclusion of unnecessarily large safety factors. Except for a few modern articles such as radio tubes, refrigerators, and automobiles, such quantitative knowledge is almost completely lacking; this is the case, for instance, in the textile and garment fields.

The third aspect of consumer specifications has to do with the testing of goods to determine their acceptability. Several kinds of problems arise. First, we have the statistical problems created by sampling errors and variability in the tests themselves. Again, we have the technological problem of carrying out enough tests economically and efficiently. But the greatest problem by far is to discover objective tests which shall be correlated with consumer requirements. Consider for example a piano, or any piece of furniture made of wood. If over a period of years the wood warps or undergoes other undesirable changes, the article will not meet the consumer's wants. We can write into our specifications the requirement, "The wood shall show no sign of warping after five years of ordinary use," but such a specification is useless alike for manufacturing and for testing. What kind of test can we apply that will not take years to complete, and will yet give us an index of quality? Unless we can find such a test, we cannot write an effective specification; we shall be unable to tell, for any particular article, whether it meets our requirements or not. Moreover, we shall be severely handicapped in our manufacturing attempts at improving quality; such attempts can hardly get very far if we have no means of recognizing quality improvement.

The economic and social consequences of quality improvement are likely to force themselves increasingly upon our attention as time goes on. Thus the modern toothbrush with synthetic bristles lasts several times as long as the old-fashioned brush. The nylon stocking outwears the silk stocking; so also with women's slips and girdles. Glassware for use in homes and restaurants is much less subject to breakage than formerly. In some fields we may reasonably expect that expanding demand will keep pace with quality improvement; thus it is possible that increased car use will balance improvements in automobile and tire manufacturing. But in general, it seems doubtful that our industry can continue much longer on the hypothesis of an expanding domestic market, and thus we encounter, as consequences of quality improvement, far-reaching social problems. Unless the analogy with other sciences is wholly misleading, these problems will be solved only by the development of a valid quantitative science in economics and sociology.

And here we meet the biggest specification of all, the specification of the kind of society we want to live in. Other specifications acquire meaning only in the light of this one. Thus if our ideal society contains large-scale industry as an essential ingredient, we must set limits to quality improvement; man's capacity to consume is unlimited, but he quickly becomes satiated with any one article. Unlimited quality improvement must lead inevitably to diversified small-scale industry, not to huge mass-production establishments. If this is the type of society we are tending to, our lawmaking, policy-making and financial groups should recognize it and prepare for it—or, if such action is desired, take measures to arrest the trend. Certainly we shall hardly achieve a good society unless we know first what a good society is, and second what we can do to get it.

The basis for progress toward these goals must be valid education. Extreme specialization, producing engineers who know no history and philosophers who know no science, can hardly cope with the intricate problems of present-day civilization. When the path is single, a tiny beam can illuminate it; as the way turns into a maze, we need illumination over a wider area. If for an integrated society we can produce men with integrated knowledge, we may reasonably hope to attain a society in which our diverse elements will function as an organic whole, if not always in harmony, yet in a state of health and growth.

ASHCROFT: Our next speaker will be PROFESSOR RALPH F. BREYER, who will address the meeting on . . .

QUESTIONS ON SPECIFICATIONS FOR CONSUMERS' GOODS FROM THE POINT OF VIEW OF MARKETING

BREYER: I want to present to you a few notes of a man primarily interested in marketing, with respect to specifications. Anyone who has had experience in college for some years must know that there are various occasions when it is more beneficial all around to reverse the formal direction of the flow of educational processes and have the class, or at least certain members of it, pour forth the edification with the teacher on the receiving end. To carry the situation over to a cognate form of education, the present panel meeting, may I say I am sure that one of these rare occasions is with us right here and now, for the only thing that I hope to do is to raise a few questions regarding certain phases of the subject, "Specifications for Consumer Goods," that seem of fundamental importance and are largely unanswered.

The student of marketing attempts to assess the importance of such a program as this to the marketing institution, and in doing this I shall assume that the term "specification" of course means "exact description

of the properties of a product," description that makes use of precisely
defined terms such as the thread count of a man's broadcloth shirt; and
I am assuming further that such specifications are set up primarily for
the guidance of the individual or the ultimate consumer in arriving at
his purchasing decision.

Now, considering specifications in this light, it is most important that
we keep clearly in mind the essential background. The major components of a purchase, when viewed externally, so to speak, are the *quality*
of the tangible product itself, the *quantity,* the incident *services,* and the
price. The product quality is but one of the components of the purchase
transaction, and specifications form only a part of it in the sense, at least,
that they are but one of several means of conveying information on the
quality of a product to the consumer. In the case of specifications, the
task can for the purpose of discussion be divided into two complemen-
tary parts: first the technical engineer's job of rating the qualities of the
products; and second, the psychological task of conveying the meaning
inherent in the quality stipulations to the individual consumer.

Now even one who is not intimately acquainted with the work can
quickly sense how much more difficult this task, especially the second
part, must be when done for the individual consumer, than when it is
performed for the industrial consumer, with his set of uses that permit
so much more opportunity of precise measurement of performance.
When the student of marketing attempts to use specifications in the
marketing field, he is likely to find his most crucial and baffling questions arising in the second part of that test, where the psychological
problems predominate. In his attempt at such an appraisal, he finds that
his thinking constantly carries him back to the four basic (perhaps I
could say obvious) questions. If we try to see what the term "specifications" means to marketing, how far it would penetrate into the fabric
of marketing, we find we are ultimately forced back to "obvious"
things.

One of these questions is: *To what extent will consumers be able to
understand the specifications?* If there are to be exact specifications, a
considerable use of technical terms would appear to be almost indis-
pensable, for the manufacturing group. If the bulk of the consumers,
or sizable groups of them, do not understand considerable portions of
such specifications, therefore their value to the consumers and to marketing is obviously greatly reduced. Of course much can undoubtedly
be done and is already being done by our educational institutions to give
the younger generation at least an understanding of many of these technical terms, but as far as I know there has been little comprehensive
consumer research to establish a definite degree of understanding of

oft-recurring technical quality terms in textile goods, housefurnishings, and other lines for all major segments of the population.

The second basic question is: *What degree of confidence do the various important segments of consumer public have in the specifications that may be set up in alternative lines of consumer goods?* This question refers solely to the specifications as such, and not the correspondence of actual goods to the specifications. Now we can be rather certain that this confidence in the specifications, like consumer confidence in a manufacturer or a retailer, will not grow of itself; it must be cultivated and nourished and protected from the attacks of those who might undermine it. Granted, of course, that in the first place the confidence is deserved, I would venture the opinion that scarcely anything would impress the marketing men more than adequate evidence of such consumer confidence in a set of specifications. Admittedly, to obtain such data by means of consumer research poses a difficulty, but probably not an insurmountable technical one. The building of such confidence will take years of great effort. How much of this burden are the consumer groups or the educational institutions ready to assume, and how much will be thrust directly upon the marketing institution? I hope not too much on the last, because it is of the nature of things that the distributor should be primarily interested in building consumer confidence in his store or wholesale house or whatever other distributing unit he owns. In any case marketing at retail levels already finds itself saddled with a very considerable sales training job, for the sales clerks should know as much about the meaning of specifications as the consumer.

The third question is: *How far is it feasible to go in using performance specifications for consumer goods when these specifications are primarily for the guidance of the consumer?* This question, of course, is related to the prior two. In some cases at least, ultimate consumers are more able to comprehend performance data cast in exact terms than material and construction information. Moreover, it would seem that the presence or absence of this type of data would constitute an important factor in getting consumer confidence in the specifications. In a comparatively limited number of instances it may be the one opportunity a consumer has of checking roughly, at least, the correspondence of the merchandise with the specifications. In view of the importance to the consumer of this element in the specifications it is a key factor in any estimate of the place and importance of specifications in marketing. In selecting prices for the Bureau of Labor Statistics' cost-of-living index, Williams reports that it was found that except for food, most of the information available on the quality of consumer goods was concerned in defining materials of which they were made and how they were constructed. There was practically no data in regard to their performance, or their value in use to the consumer. Now were such data included, the retail section of marketing would be greatly concerned to see that the performance specifications were precisely and clearly stated, and did not permit too broad a range of issues, because this is the one element that is likely to cause complaints, allowances, returns, and disgruntled customers, and it does not matter to retailing whether the customer is wrong or not so far as damage to good will and profits are concerned.

The last question, and perhaps the most important one is: *What is the role played by specifications in the mental processes that determine the consumer's decision to buy or not to buy?* That is the point on which marketing men constantly have their thoughts and eyes focused, and of course it is all-inclusive of the other factors. A group of research specialists held a meeting to decide on the subject of rational consumer buying. Part of their conclusions is interesting in this connection. There were tests for durability, color, etc., they were all available in some degree, but so far are offered in such a disorganized way that the buyer is confronted with the problem of selecting between systems of standards as well as the problem of making judgments under the system of standards that he selects. But the question is: Just what part do specifications play in fact, and not as a matter of opinion? What can be done by scientific consumer research to answer this query depends almost entirely on the limits of our knowledge of the workings of man's mind, and psychologists have already discussed the possibility and probability of this type of research. For the student of marketing who attempts to appraise the specifications in his field, this is a crucial question because so many marketing matters, especially in retailing, depend upon its answer, such as retail advertising, sales-training programs, the extension of self-service, and a score of others.

Finally, it should not be forgotten that specifications constitute only one of the ways of conveying quality information to the consumers. Others well-known are brands, general descriptions either oral or written, informative labels that contain more exact descriptions with some use of standard definitions of terms, commercial standards or grades and certifications, not to mention certain combinations of these. To a marketing student it certainly appears urgent that, as far and as soon as possible, it be determined objectively for the more important market situations which of these alternative systems of quality designations is the more effective as an agency for informing ultimate consumers of quality merchandise. Moreover, the picture from the marketing point of view would still be far from complete unless we include service as well as tangible products in our study of specifications and other quality designation systems.

I have in mind more particularly the auxiliary services involved in the sale of tangible products to the ultimate consumer, although they constitute only a part of those that might prove worthy of consideration. Services are by no means so individualized that specifications have no general application to them. Two good examples would be "credit" and "product guarantees." Consumer installment credit, in peacetime, often has a life of six months to two years, while guarantees have often a life of a year. In the former case, much trade effort has already gone into the setting of the specifications in the form of suitable installment contract terms, in so far as these have not already been determined by law.

The questions I have raised pose, of course, tremendous practical difficulties, not the least of which are caused by the ever-increasing pace of the kaleidoscopic changes in production, the material construction and use, and also the many and varied interests and points of view of the parties concerned. Progress in the field of specifications and related quality-designation systems depends in great part on the four questions I have posed. I venture to say that progress, if sound, will be facilitated and expedited in direct proportion to the development of specifications and other quality-designation systems. Such progress will be anchored firmly to the consumers, through full recognition of the various differences among various segments of consumers, and will come about in direct proportion to our ability to develop scientific consumer research methods which can objectively establish the consumer situations, so to speak, and also in direct proportion to our developing a broad point of view that embraces all types of quality-designation systems, and the possible contribution of each.

ASHCROFT: LIEUTENANT J. H. CURTISS will discuss . . .

THE GOVERNMENT'S USE OF SPECIFICATIONS FOR CONSUMERS' GOODS

CURTISS: As many of you know, my main interest and experience in working for consumer groups has been totally on the engineering side of the business. I found myself swimming today in an entirely unexpected atmosphere of philosophy and sociology in which I feel quite incompetent to render any really important contribution. It seemed to me, however, that I can say one or two words about the Government as a consumer.

We hear a great deal about consumer groups, but we do not often

hear mentioned in discussions such as these that the Government probably constitutes the largest consumer group in the country. Government
regulations are such that in its purchasing activities it is forced to make
heavy use of written specifications. I am probably repeating things you
all know when I state that in general, where purchases of value greater
than $100 are involved, invitations to bid must normally be sent out, and
with these there must be written specifications. Hence the great development of Federal specifications and those issued by various individual
Government agencies. Now let's discuss the aspects of specifications
listed by my distinguished colleague Professor Peach, as they pertain
to Government specifications.

First, there is the question of determining the needs of the consumer.
In the present instance we seem to have a considerable simplification
of the problem. For example, what does the Navy need? Let's exclude
ordnance from discussion in this problem, and from any of the other
problems listed by Mr. Peach, as the needs of ordnance are highly specialized, and besides I don't know much about them. In so far as purchase specifications are concerned, the needs of the Navy Department
Bureau of Ships (where I was attached) are simply the needs of a contractor, a builder, or a manufacturer, for raw materials and finished
components for the construction and fabrication of buildings and en-
gines of war. The question of the need for such fabrication is largely a
matter of military strategy and national policy, and does not seem to fall
into the realm of consumer-research or market analysis.

Another item in Mr. Peach's list—the last item—I can dispose of
very rapidly also. It is the sociological impact of the specifications. Here
I simply throw up my hands; I have no intelligent comments to offer
concerning the sociological impact of the Government's purchase specifications.

Let's return to the second item on Mr. Peach's list, the operational
translation of consumer need into acceptance criteria. As I see it, only
engineering problems are involved here in general, but they are very
serious ones. The problem of trying to get standard methods of test to
mean something from the point of view of the ultimate use of the materials is a matter of continual concern in the writing of Government
specifications. I believe that one-half or three-quarters of the Government testing research is being devoted to that sort of problem in peace-
time. For instance, take the question of the usual psysical tests that we
have for textiles. Mr. Ashcroft has written about the lack of correlation
that exists here, such as that between tensile tests and the actual needs
of the consumer. I feel that a great deal more work remains to be done in
this area. Consider metallurgical products such as brass rods or steel

armor plate or high-tensile steel plate for building ships. The classical tests here are tensile strength and hardness, but taking, for example, the brass rod, how does anyone know that performance in the tensile tests really has anything to do with the ultimate use of the brass rod? I believe that tensile strength often has very little to do with consumer needs. In other words, for the most usual or customary uses of wrought brass, the tensile strength and hardness seem to have little correlation with performance use. Thus even in such a well-established field as metallurgical testing, the problem of the definition of "good" and "bad" needs a great deal more work put on it. Of course there are some cases where we know pretty well that we have a test which represents what might be considered as the end use of a material. Some service life tests aren't too bad.

To take up chemicals, consider the matter of determining the quality of soap or synthetic detergents. There chiefly all we have is chemical analysis to determine whether the material is "good" or "bad." Washing tests seem to be quite unsatisfactory. What is clean cloth and what is dirty cloth? A great deal of research can be done on soap alone to determine what kind of tests would best identify the soap that fills the given consumer needs. To sum up, I feel that this problem of operational translation of consumer needs is a tremendous field in the theory of the Government's purchases, and needs further investigation, more so than any other problem.

In comparison to it, the study of acceptance criteria and what to do about them is relatively simple. That statement may seem odd in the light of the widespread advertising that has been given to applications of statistical methods to specification work, and to inspection under specifications. Nevertheless the problem of deciding what to do about inspection engineering in connection with specifications is practically completely solved, as compared to the problem of deciding how a test should be correlated with what we really want.

It is true, however, that in the matter of supplying acceptance or inspection instructions for Government specifications there are two schools of thought as to how inspection instructions and sampling plans should be promulgated in connection with specifications. Both of these schools were really of opportunistic origin. They simply grew up in accordance with what was a convenient thing to do under differing circumstances. One school of thought insists that specifications should have their own inspection clauses (that is, the number of samples, size of samples, and all that type of material) directly written into the specification. Another extreme view is that none of this acceptance-requirement material should be published in the specification; that is, that the acceptance specification should never be promulgated in connection with the design specification. Rather, it should be sprung on the contractor after he has bid and the bid has been accepted. Obviously the latter involves one in certain legal difficulties which during the war could be surmounted rather easily by high-pressure expediters and dignified and dangerous-looking senior officers in charge of Government field inspection offices. In peacetime, I believe, the difficulties would be more serious.

I advocate neither one plan nor the other, that is, neither the complete writing-out of the acceptance requirements into the same pamphlet with the design specifications, nor the omission of the sampling plans from specifications entirely. I think the best way is to promulgate inside the specification specific methods of test, and specific sample sizes or maximum sample sizes, where *destructive* tests are involved. Where non-destructive tests are involved and the set-up of facilities therefore are not expensive at all for the contractors to provide, then I believe that the Government agency's own specifications-unit can spring the sampling plan on the contractor without prior warning. In other words, the contractor does not need to see the sampling-plan written out into the specification in such cases.

But this is no place to emphasize further this detail of specification theory. I think the main things to emphasize are the following: (1) The problems of ascertaining consumer needs, of the writing of appropriate acceptance criteria, and of the sociological aspects of the specification are perhaps less urgent problems in the case of Government specifications than in the case of nongovernment specifications; (2) that the problem of operational translation of the consumer needs is very serious indeed in the case of government specifications, and needs much further study.

ASHCROFT: The last speaker is MR. D. H. PALMER, who is going to talk on . . .

THE NEED OF INSTITUTIONAL BUYERS IN RELATION TO THE PROBLEM OF CONSUMER WANTS

PALMER: I will be as brief as possible and will emphasize two or three points that may have already been covered in part. There are, I believe, two general classes of buyers—one, the ultimate consumer or the person who buys a product for his own use; the second type is exemplified by a Government procurement agency which buys for the use of other persons or departments. This latter type of buyer may never see how the product is used and may, therefore, not have close contact with it.

The institutional buyer falls into the second class. He is, as a rule, closer to the point of end use than most state or federal buyers and is therefore likely to be more familiar with actual serviceability requirements.

Much has been said in this Conference about measuring the desires and needs of those who buy and consume. Some attention, I believe, should be given to the problem of need; that is, how are basic needs to be determined and to what extent do commodities meet these needs. For the hospital buyer the need is best met by those products which give maximum serviceability where that includes adaptability to end use as well as durability. While end use should be the sole criterion for judging the quality of a given product, many other factors frequently determine the type and quality of the purchased article.

There has been much emphasis placed on measuring consumer interest or finding out what he thinks he wants. Unfortunately, in too many cases the buyer or the consumer does not know his exact needs, has warped notions about what he wants, and is uninformed about the capabilities of the manufacturer to produce the product that will best meet his requirements.

Let me give a few examples of factors which frequently hinder hospital buyers in procuring those commodities which are best adapted for a particular end use. Doctors too often specify certain brands of surgical products based more on prejudice and limited experience than on a scientific knowledge of the qualities of the product. For example, one widely sold brand of surgeons' blades is most frequently specified despite the fact that there is no evidence to show it is superior. Some purchasing agents have found it possible to introduce a new and less well-known blade only when the doctor is unaware of the brand. In such instances the doctor failed to make complaints until he happened to find out that he was not getting his preferred brand.

The prestige factor is often more important in buying than actual quality. We often find that indifferently constructed surgical masks are used by doctors and nurses in hospitals, apparently for the sake of appearance only. Masks should be constructed and worn to give maximum filtering efficiency, but considering the types used and the way they are worn, their only function apparently is to give the impression that professional practice is being followed.

The questions of bad judgment and misinformation are also determining factors in deciding on a given purchase. Hospitals buy many gallons of vaporizing type deodorizers which may act as a mask for odors but cannot possibly eliminate the odors as claimed. One widely sold brand contains chlorophyll and formaldehyde. The chlorophyll is not volatile and therefore can have no effect on odors, while the only possible effect of formaldehyde is to desensitize the olfactory nerve. In such instances the lack of precise knowledge about a product and what it will do results in unscientific and uneconomical purchasing.

It not infrequently happens that a completely satisfactory product is unavailable. My organization has for years tested clinical thermometers on a large scale. Although all such clinical thermometers carry a statement that they meet the requirements of Commercial Standard CS1–42, we have found failures running from 45% to 47% in every test. At the moment we do not know of a single brand which will consistently meet the standard. We do know that satisfactory thermometers are being purchased by Federal agencies; hospitals apparently receive second- and third-grade instruments which will not meet the requirements set up by agencies enforcing strict compliance rules.

One often hears the statement that one gets what one pays for. In actual practice we find in our buying that one gets what one pays for only when one knows his product and frequently tests against specified requirements. Price is not necessarily a criterion of quality. Those who buy on this basis frequently pass up products because of their low prices. We have found hospitals refusing to buy a high quality waterproof sheeting at 65¢ a yard because they expected that good quality sheeting came at $1.50 per yard. A certain brand of surgical soap selling at $1.40 per pound of dry soap sells in greater quantities to hospitals than another soap at 39¢ per pound—a soap which is equal in quality. In this instance an imposing name, as well as high price, seems more important to the buyer than economy. These illustrations will show that when one measures consumer interest he may or may not be determining basic needs but rather preference based on prejudice, misinformation, or lack of information.

What then do we wish to measure? If we are interested in improving the status of the consumer, our measurements, it seems to me, should be to determine basic needs and industry's ability to meet them rather than superficial mass reactions of consumers. We need to know a great deal more about what society's requirements are in the way of serviceability for the products used and how those requirements can be met.

Our lack of knowledge regarding adaptability and serviceability of products with respect to their end use is astounding. No problem in the field of commodity research is more important and has received less attention. There are, for example, no studies which give a conclusive answer to the question of the comparative life of the different types of sheets. From the standpoint of economy and satisfactory service, should the consumer or the institutional buyer purchase percales or heavyweight or mediumweight muslins? We do not know the answer, although probably no commodity has been subjected to more extensive routine laboratory tests than sheeting.

We cannot expect consumers to give us reliable answers to questions related to their needs. Such answers will come only from exhaustive technical studies made by those who are competent to judge all the factors involved. Consumer advice and coöperation is required, but only the engineer can carry out the research work involving an analysis of end use requirements and the fabrication of materials to best meet these requirements.

DISCUSSION

RUBIN: I think some work that my company has been doing in the psychological aspects of consumer buying will be of interest to this panel. It parallels pretty much the entire discussion today on "Why Do People Buy." It is, of course, very common knowledge that people do not always buy rationally. We have seen time and time again how people will buy an item which they know is definitely inferior to another item. Because it appeals to them more they will buy it, and consequently we have developed a technique called "Sense Qualities Research." We have applied it quite successfully to a number of consumer products—cigarettes, beer, and some others too. Certainly it has its shortcomings, but I think there is a considerable field for it.

We found in our experiments that the general consumer public does not have the ability to articulate sufficiently; they aren't able to translate their thoughts, their reasons why they buy, into sufficiently precise terms to be of use to the manufacturers of consumer goods. So we have developed a list of terms that do describe the various sense qualities. A product may affect the sense of taste, of smell, of sight, or texture (that is, "feel"), and we give the consuming public an opportunity to describe their reactions, or the reasons why they like or dislike something from the list, in far more precise terms than anything they will give us themselves. We have not as yet applied the method to shoes, but we have applied it very successfully to Mr. Peach's other example of cigarettes, and our manufacturing clients have found it very helpful in changing their formula. We were able to tell them that to the consuming public the brand was too strong; when the formula was changed there were indications that ours was good advice.

Of course all these things are more or less involved as a matter of promotion, but I think that we have definitely made a step in the problem of stating consumer specifications in such terms that the manufacturers can use them.

PHILLIPS: Mr. Chairman, I want to thank the panel this morning for at least raising what seem to me the central problems that are involved in the whole consumer movement. I think Mr. Palmer was the first person in the entire Conference who used the word "needs," and it seems to be the central thing in our whole economy. When we realize that the income of industry is paid by consumers, and that when any group of consumers buys any product it pays the salaries and the bonuses of the management, the wages of workers, the prices paid for the labor of producing the raw materials, the interest, the dividends, the net rent, the royalties, and putting the monies in the corporation reserves—then we see the true relation between industry and the consumer.

Now here is a conference called with a group of philosophers who were not even able to define a consumer. It seems to me that the definition of a consumer is very simple. The consumer is everybody. The consumer is not the worker, because all workers, although they are consumers, do not include the aged or whoever worked and produced everything that we have and are entitled to a dignified life in their old age. The worker does not include the child who will be the worker of the future. So the consumer is the entire population, and to represent or to study consumer preferences is no problem at all. To study consumer wants is no problem. The main problem is: What are the needs of the American people and how can they be satisfied through the spending of the billions of dollars that constitute the total aggregate expenditures of the people, or the nation as consumers?

Now Professor Peach began at the end of this conference to throw out in a tentative form the problem which has been evaded in this conference because it has been conducted almost entirely for the seller of the goods, from the standpoint of the man who has something to sell and is looking at his little bit of a narrow segment of a great human problem which really concerns itself with the common welfare of the American people.

STROGAR: Mr. Peach spoke about the proposed education revision which would include a broad basis from which specifications would branch. Are there any specific plans for such a program?

PEACH: In some fields we already have a tradition that before a man engages in a special study he is expected to have a couple of years of special education. Personally I'd like to see the growth of a point of view that people who intend entering the engineering school approach it so that they have a little cultural background in history, economics, and all the things that engineers tend to neglect, but are so important if we consider the place of engineering in society. But I don't know that any organized program is under way to effect such a thing.

PALMER: There is one point that I'd like to mention. We have really emphasized the need for technical education on consumer goods. Unfortunately all research seems to be in the hands of industry itself, and I think it is high time that our universities started programs along this line. We need our engineering department to go into consumer durable goods, and we need our universities and possibly our Federal and state agencies entering into this general subject. I am astonished to find, after analyzing the courses given in purchasing in the various colleges, that there is not one that emphasizes standards in those courses. They do not emphasize the most basic questions of all: the basic question of quality that you are going to get.

SAMPLING TECHNIQUES

PARTICIPANTS

CHAIRMAN: Morris Hansen, *Bureau of the Census*. SPEAKERS: Samuel G. Barton, *Industrial Surveys Co., Inc.;* A. N. Watson, *Curtis Publishing Co.;* W. Edwards Deming, *Bureau of the Budget*. DISCUSSION: Alfred Politz, *Alfred Politz Research;* Frederick F. Stephan, *Cornell University*.

HANSEN: The subject of sampling techniques can be conceived pretty broadly or narrowed down, and I think perhaps because the broader scope of it has been considered at the other meetings, the panel here may want to restrict itself to a more narrow approach to the problem.

Sampling techniques in general can be regarded as dealing with the entire problem of inference, and actually deal with that problem even in this narrow setting, but I think perhaps most of the emphasis in this discussion might be in problems of a finite population, to ascertain the characteristics of that population, although the members of the panel might want to broaden beyond that. This problem certainly changes the scope from a general one of broad inference. At least, I think the restriction here will be in terms of errors of sampling in survey design, rather than other types of errors which perhaps are equal or of greater importance, or more serious problems in connection with survey design in the measuring of consumer preferences.

I'll call first on MR. S. G. BARTON, of Industrial Surveys, to make a few general remarks on . . .

CONSUMER PANELS

BARTON: As more knowledge of sampling methods is gained, it becomes apparent that considerable effort will be required to demonstrate to industry the advantages and ultimate economy of employing sound sampling systems despite apparent costs, which are considerably higher than those to which industry has been accustomed. It is very likely true that industry can be educated to better sampling operations if we demonstrate that not only are the costs fully warranted but that the improved systems are flexible in the sense that they can be quickly designed for a variety of consumer research problems and successfully carried out in the field by interviewers who are of limited skill and responsibility. Certain practical problems must be solved:

1. Experience shows us that the interviewer cannot be entrusted with the assignment of distributing his interviews in a random manner. It follows that the fieldworker then must be given assignments to call upon specific people—families, dwellings, stores, etc.—which have been obtained by some random means, presumably in the offices of the statistician or research director. In this connection, a problem of apparent cost arises when it is found that the cost in the field per interview for preselected cases is several times in excess of the cost per case of the unscientific, uncontrolled chance selection systems to which the consumer research industry is accustomed.

2. An additional practical problem affecting costs which must be considered is the natural tendency of the average interviewer, working without close supervision, to fail to follow through in completing each specific interview or case, according to the design of the sample. These practical problems frequently arise under such conditions as when the random sample assigns the interviewer to climbing a long flight of stairs, interviewing suspicious people, people who do not fluently speak the interviewer's language, or when consent to an interview must be obtained through a domestic, by means of an ill-functioning speaking tube or communication system in apartment buildings, or where the approach is made difficult by unfriendly dogs or friendly dogs with muddy feet.

3. An additional problem of similar type is that of completing interviews with people who are never accessible during normal working hours.

4. Most researchers are familiar with the existence of a similar set of field problems when it is attempted to collect data from consumers by means of mail questionnaires. In such surveys, while a random sample may be designed for outgoing mailings, that portion of the sample returning questionnaires will no longer be random. These problems tend to work against the operating success of random sampling in consumer research and should, as far as possible, be recognized by the statistician in the design of the experiment and in the interpretation of the result.

To overcome these problems, considerable effort has been made by many researchers along three lines:

1. Design of the random sample to give maximum consideration to the need for tight field supervision.

2. Development of systems which, while basically random, permit of some limited substitution in the field, without increasing the error.

3. Development of highly stratified systems with the objective of obtaining cells within which the variance is low enough to permit of arbitrary or biased selections of the respondents or cases to be used within any given cell.

The above problems of field application are of a general nature in the area of measuring consumer interest. During the past eight years there has been a growing realization of the need for a particular type of continuous consumer measurement commonly known as consumer panels. The essential element of consumer panels is that data are drawn continuously or repetitively from the same respondents described as a static sample. The contribution of this technique is that data covering the behavior of people or families relating to a considerable time span can be obtained which far exceed the human ability to recall at any particular moment, as in a single interview.

The design of a sample for a panel operation, however, presents particular problems since most forms of panel operations are based fundamentally upon the ability and willingness of the respondents themselves to keep records of their day-to-day activities. This fundamental difficulty results in a biased sample of people since (1) not all people will begin to keep such records, and (2) of those who begin keeping records, a portion drops out.

In 1941, working experimentally in Evansville, Indiana, we stratified the city by geographical sections and by rental zones within sections. From the City Directory a random selection of dwellings was then obtained within each rental zone. Of the total sample so selected, about 47% began to keep continuous records. Tabulations of several factors such as automobile ownership, occupation of members, and possession of utilities showed significant differences between the participating group and the group which refused to start. In addition, inventories of a variety of food and drug products in both groups showed significant differences as well.

Six months later about 20% of the total or original random sample were still keeping records of food and drug purchases. Segregating this group, it was found that many of their characteristics varied significantly from those who had started but dropped out, and varied significantly as well from those of the original random sample.

This condition, inherent with the panel technique, appears to make unworkable a fully randomized sample and has led members of our staff into extensive experimentation toward developing highly stratified samples as suggested above.

At the present time the National Consumer Panel of Industrial Surveys Company has developed a quota system which is designed for five thousand families, wherein the United States is divided into forty-one districts of which fifteen are represented by cities of 500,000 or more population and the twin cities of Minneapolis-St. Paul. Within the remaining twenty-five areas population quotas were then estimated for up to three city sizes: farms, places under 100,000 population, and cities of 100,000 to 500,000 population. Population quotas were then estimated for each of three age-levels within each city as well as within each city size within each district. Populations were then estimated within three educational levels within each of the age groups, resulting in 745 sampling cells.

In the recruiting of additional and replacement families, several independent controls within geographic districts are employed as well. This system is based primarily upon analysis of five years' historical data on the performance and characteristics of products and comparisons with manufacturers' shipment data. We suspect that the panel derives greater estimating accuracy from control of the above four factors than from any other four that might be employed.

Since full random methods cannot be used, any estimates of accuracy had to be obtained by making direct comparisons of panel projections with other estimates of the same universe. In general there are error limits of five to fifteen per cent on most products for which the panel is designed to yield estimates.

I'd like to show you some of the charts. Figure 1 will not excite the statisticians. These comparisons are actual and real and are based upon historical data, but we don't know how accurate we may be next year. The panel may be much further off than it would seem to be at this point. In making a comparison between the projections of panel data, and projection per capita together with manufacturers' shipments, we have, of course, to get them on a comparable basis so far as is possible. Unfortunately we have to estimate manufacturers' shipments as well, and in so doing there are several major adjustments required, primarily of two types.

The first is adjusting manufacturers' shipments to allow for changes in inventory between two periods of time. If you want to estimate sales to consumers during this time span you have to correct for possible changes in inventory at the wholesale, institutional, and retail levels. The second one is determination of what portion of a manufacturer's shipments never do find their way into consumers' homes, that is, industrial and institutional consumption and shipments out of the country.

Figure 2 is a list of adjustments. Short-term comparisons are difficult

PANEL PROJECTIONS
VS.
MANUFACTURERS SHIPMENTS
Two major adjustments are required
1·Change of Inventory Levels*
Period I
Period II
WHOLESALE
INSTITUTIONS
RETAIL
NORMAL LEVEL
2·Proportion of Shipments to non-civilian home consumers
A·Average Proportion
B·Change in Proportion
* INCLUDING CHANGING NUMBERS OF WHOLESALERS & RETAILERS

FIG. 1

PANEL PROJECTIONS
VS.
MANUFACTURERS SHIPMENTS
Check List of Adjustments
1·Mfg. Shipments to Foreign & I&I users
2·Mfg. Shipments to Government
3·Wholesaler sales to Foreign & I&I users
4·Wholesaler sales to Government
5·Retailer sales to small I&I users
6·Retailer transfers to other retailers
7·Retailer sales to members of Armed Forces & Institutions

FIG. 2

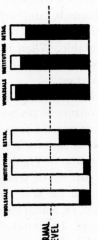

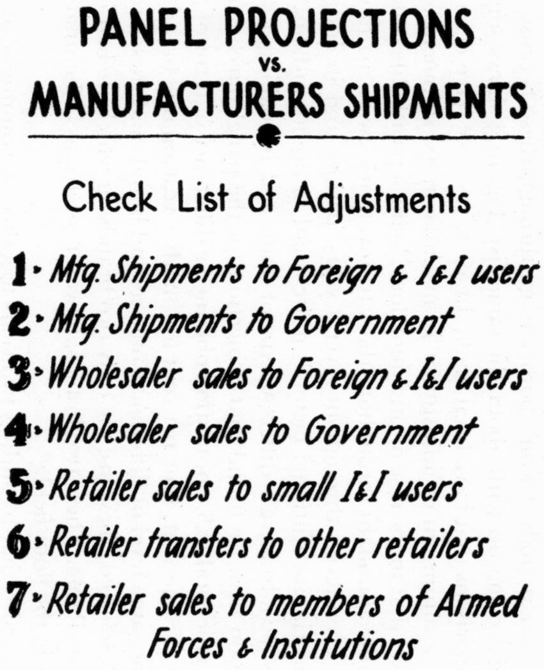

to make. Most of these that I will show you have to do with one- or two- or three-year periods. I won't bother to go through these because I am sure you'd come up with about the same list. Figure 3 shows some of the comparisons that have been made. In a few cases we have been able to make a minimum of adjustment in manufacturers' shipments. The reason was that in the case of premium flour, being a perishable product, it was quite abundant throughout the war; inventories were maintained at fairly even levels throughout several years' period; and in addition, the industrial-institutional factor is quite small in premium flour. Restaurants have to have a different type of flour, and in making a direct comparison here we found that projections of the panel purchases per capita to the total U.S. population obtained a difference of error of three per cent for one year, four per cent for another year on one brand, and about the same level of differences on a second brand, and these are not carefully selected; these are the only two brands on which we had information available. These two brands, however, pretty well dominate the business in the flour field.

We find also that by adding two years together, as you might suspect, the differences or disagreements between the panel and the manufacturer's shipments were brought closer together. That perhaps was due to elimination of some variation in inventory. In making other comparisons we have had to be careful of the changing level of distribution. This manufacturer (Figure 4) reflects a company that was expanding its distribution, opening new channels, and supplying the pipelines with additional products, so it was necessary to wait for a stabilized period before comparison was available. When it was, a year's panel projections came within about two and three per cent on two brands on which we were able to make comparison.

Another type of comparison that has been possible is that of comparing projections with government tax withdrawals, as in margarine, where the manufacturer must pay the tax on margarine as he produces it instead of as he sells it. So we find for several years back that the production shown in the heavy line in Figure 5 exceeds the consumption (light line) during the first part of the year, and the reverse happens in the second part of the year. For the year's total there is an error of less than one and a half per cent, or actual disagreement between the two data of one and a half per cent. This kind of agreement has been found every year for several years. We don't do so well on an individual product or individual brand which we have been able to compare. This is the only case of brand comparison, and our error seems to be about twelve per cent.

Another comparison was available as recorded by National Canners

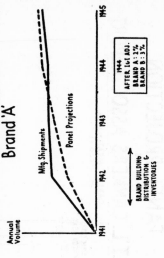

PANEL PROJECTIONS
vs.
CLIENTS SALES

Extended Time Period Corrects Inventory Change
1942-1943 (small tɩl factor)

Brand 'A'

	1942	Error 1943	Two Years
	3%	4%	1%

Brand 'B'

	1942	Error 1943	Two Years
	1.5%	1.8%	.3%

$M_D = .7\%$

FIG. 3. PREMIUM FLOUR

PANEL PROJECTIONS
vs.
CLIENT SALES

Extended Time Period Corrects Distribution Change

Brand 'A'

Annual Volume

Mfg. Shipments

Panel Projections

1941 1942 1943 1944 1945

BRAND BUILDING
DISTRIBUTION &
INVENTORIES

1944
AFTER 1st ADJ.
BRAND A: 2%
BRAND B: 3%

FIG. 4. DEHYDRATED SOUP

161

PANEL PROJECTION
vs.
U.S. MARGARINE TAX WITHDRAWALS

Diff 1.5%
Small 1 v 1 factor

FIG. 5. MARGARINE

PANEL PROJECTION
vs.
NAT'L. CANNERS ASSOC. REPORT

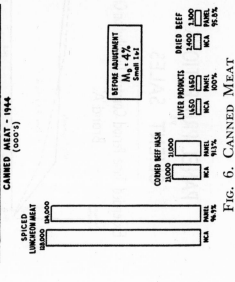

CANNED MEAT - 1944
(000's)

BEFORE ADJUSTMENT
$M_0 = 4\%$
Small 1 v 1

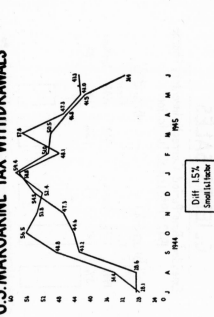

FIG. 6. CANNED MEAT

Association (Figure 6). These estimates, as many of you know, and some of these agreements may be completely fortuitous. Because it is not a random sample we are forced into this kind of comparison to try to get some working knowledge of the probable accuracies of the data.

Here (referring to chart) we have an average difference of about four per cent for some of the small items as well as some of the larger ones, and in addition some of these products are what we call class types, that is, the higher the economic level the greater the purchase, and some are the reverse type. In comparison with drug sales in a personal-care type of product we obtained differences of one to ten per cent on three brands for a year's period and about the same for several years.

Two years ago our staff embarked upon a long-term project of developing a panel sample design using analysis of variance. This work is carried on under the direction of Paul Ozanne, Chief of the Mathematical Statistics Department. While there are several more years of work ahead of us, a number of sampling efficiencies have already resulted. The present panel sample designs evidently now estimate the movement of an extended list of food and drug products and the incidence of magazines, newspapers, and radio programs within workable limits of accuracy.

The furtherance of the analysis of variance should serve efficiently to increase accuracy in the estimation of regional analyses as well. In other words, the work is just beginning, and we think that over a period of years this particular case of qualitative type research may yield quite workable and reasonably reliable sets of data.

HANSEN: I'll ask DR. A. N. WATSON now to present his talk on . . .

WHAT'S AHEAD IN STATISTICAL SAMPLING AS APPLIED TO MARKET RESEARCH

WATSON: Those of us who make a living buying the results of research surveys would be very much surprised to see a presentation that did not use the phrase "national cross section" in describing the sample taken. It would be like hearing a political speech that failed to promise lower taxes, reduced debt, and greater social benefits.

In common parlance, "national cross section" means that at least some interviews were taken west of the Mississippi River. If, in addition, the interviews were apportioned by color, age, sex, and income as reported in the 1940 Census, it removes the last shadow of doubt that we can take the results of the survey and recommend action to our Board of Directors. Or does it?

The statistician doesn't think so. Unfortunately, his doubts are expressed in technical journals, interspersed with symbols of integral calculus. He keeps talking about characteristic functions, variance analysis, the statistical universe, standard errors, and confidence intervals. What we really want to know is, "Do we have a good sample or don't we?" And in turn the Board asks us, "Will this survey help us to pay next year's dividend?"

There is our current position, as I see it. We in marketing are five years behind the new statistical developments. And the statisticians are almost as far behind our real marketing needs.

Is there a way out of this situation? What can marketers do short of becoming statisticians? Is there any way in which our statistical friends can suggest improvements in marketing research that can be taken out and used in our next survey? I don't propose to bring you categorical answers to these problems, but it might be helpful to take five minutes and be more specific.

In every consumer survey there are at least five parts:

1. Initial selection of doorbells to be rung.
2. Decide what do so far as the sample is concerned if no response, or if interview is interrupted.
3. Plan the interviewing situation, once you get your foot in the door and reach the ear of the respondent.
4. Summarize data.
5. Select and present those facts which are relevant to the original problem.

The primary application of our topic today of sampling comes in devising a plan for selecting doorbells. What happens after that is also a concern of the statistician, but his first big job is to plan our approach to our respondents—in other words, to help us pick the right doorbells to be rung in the first instance.

You are all familiar with the quota method of selecting respondents. We find 10 per cent of the population in Region A, so we allocate 10 per cent of our interviews there. Likewise we instruct our interviewers that certain proportions of men will be chosen and that so many returns must be had in specified age groups. When it comes to incomes, the going gets a little tougher. What we finally tell our interviewers must come from our crystal ball, that essential tool of the more successful market researchers.

To my knowledge, there does not exist now, nor has there ever existed in this country, data on income adequate to use as a control device for consumer surveys of the general population. I say this, having in mind the 1936 Consumer Purchase Study, the 1940 Census, and recent surveys by the Bureau of Labor Statistics.

If we wish to add to our problems, we need think only of trying to find data useful for control by occupation, keeping in mind the changes that have taken place since 1940.

I need not multiply these examples before this group. But am I speaking of an obsolete technique used only by the die-hards of the marketing profession? Not at all. I am referring to the difficulties inherent in a method which probably controls 95 per cent or more of the market research done in this country. This is a live problem. Fortunately our sins usually don't catch up with us. But once in a while we have a national election, or a decennial census, or an exact count by the manufacturer of his total national sales. A check is then provided on our sampling methods. Fortunate, too, is the fact that muddling along as we do with quota controls, the results usually are not too far off, so far as we are able to tell.

But what brings out the gray hair in the statistician's head is the fact that the quota method provides no means of estimating just how far off we might be in any survey. On the other hand, there may be something to be said for the argument that we have spent our money and now we should take our results and make the best of it.

Now, along comes the sampling expert and says, "You fellows are crossing the prairie in a covered wagon. Let us sell you a 1947 model survey special. It's equipped with area selectors and built-in variance meters. It has low upkeep and is guaranteed to solve your problems. If you worry and like awake nights thinking about the next board meeting, forget it, and rest easy—your troubles are over."

At this point my mind carries me back to this technical siren song which I heeded in 1940. Anxious to get the jump on all our competitors, we procured maps from the Census Bureau and selected at random a list of approximately six thousand small areas, counting blocks in cities of fifty thousand population and over, and census enumeration districts outside these cities. This was before 1940 Census of population counts were available, so as our staff members had occasion to travel in various parts of the country, I asked them to visit their sample areas and report what they found.

I'll never forget the report from Minneapolis. In the dozen or so areas allocated to that city, I had hit the state institution for the feeble-minded as one area, and a nice grassy plot in the suburbs neatly placed between the two lanes of a super highway as another one. From that point on, what we had been calling a pioneer venture in area sampling was thereafter referred to as "Watson's folly." Fortunately, about that time Uncle Sam beckoned with a job with a somewhat higher priority.

Fortunately also, while private research facilities were curtailed, the war demanded greater activity on the part of Government agencies. The contributions which the Census Bureau had made to area sampling theory were called upon for a practical test. You all know what a fine job they have done in this field.

Where then, do we stand today? Where do we go from here?

In my opinion we are on the threshold of an important transition period. I predict that within five years most field surveys in marketing research will be made on the basis of area-sampling techniques or some modification which utilizes that basic principle.

Let me indicate briefly why I think so. Quota sampling methods are used now for two very good reasons: (1) the customer or buyer of research continues to pay for it. (2) Relatively few personnel in market research today have sufficient technical knowledge to lay out an area sample.

A student without mathematical or statistical training beyond the high-school level can be taught to lay out a quota sample in a short time and with a low cost. To plan the same operation for area sampling requires the services of a specialist and a considerable expenditure of funds for maps and other equipment. To take fullest advantage of recent advances in area-sampling theory requires such a combination of both training and experience that the demand for personnel far exceeds the supply. My estimate of five years, then, is the time required for universities to begin to turn out students with sufficient training to do the area-sampling job and for buyers of market research to begin to demand it. If there are students in this audience, I could recommend this field of study as having sure-fire job potentialities upon graduation.

When consumers of research data begin to realize that there is a practical advantage in using technically superior tools, they will not hesitate to ask and pay for them. When they discover that the term "planned confidence intervals" is nothing more than quality control applied to research production, they will understand why it is used; and finally, when they cannot only be given a set of facts but also be told how much reliance can be placed on them, market research will have attained a new and higher level of significance for business management.

These advances are not possible with quota-sampling procedures used by most market researchers today, but they do appear to be within reach in the near future by the diligent application of area sampling methods. The words "national cross section" will then have real significance and validity. The national manufacturer may well say to himself, "Here, truly, is a reliable picture of my national market."

HANSEN: I'd like to ask DR. W. E. DEMING to give a few remarks on . . .

RANDOM SAMPLES AND BIASED SAMPLES

DEMING: I am tremendously impressed always with the variety and multitude of problems in market research. They are all different, many of them are tremendously so. I am always pleased with the frank way in which marketing men are willing to discuss these problems.

I think that Mr. Barton is to be commended on the fine presentation he has made. I went through his Chicago office once and I was deeply impressed with the very careful work that he is doing there. I am sure that he is able to provide the answers to a lot of market research, but I don't know just what problems he can get at best and solve through mail response with a selected list to start with, and no interview follow-up. No one knows how premiums affect the answers. I wish I knew, and I am sure he is just as much interested as I am in finding out what the limitations of his methods are, and in finding ways of bolstering up these limitations where necessary.

We must keep some things in mind about comparisons between sample and complete count. Unfortunately, in addition to some of the things I said this morning about comparisons, there is another thing to keep in mind and that is that the public—and that includes your clients—will remember one mistake to a thousand successes. It is safer to depend on proper procedures than on comparisons and thus to eliminate the risk of a failure.

Now on this matter of stratification and controls, it is certainly true that if you stratify to the point where you have one member in a class and then could take a sample from every class, there will not be any doubt about the results; you would then have a total coverage and you would have your information if it's possible to get answers to your questions. But in sampling I'm skeptical about this matter of controls. As I said this morning, sometimes they do more harm than good, and I don't know how to find out in advance what is going to happen. I wish I did know. There is an article that I think many people don't know about, published in 1926 by two excellent Italian statisticians, Gini and Galvani. The situation was this. The census of 1929 or 1930 was going to be taken, and they still had on hand the cards for the previous census. However, they had to make room for more cards because they didn't have a great deal of space. But though they were forced to get rid of the cards for the last census, they did want to save a sample. Professors Gini and Galvani found twenty-nine counties that in fifteen respects had exactly (or closely) the same averages, percentages, proportions, and so on, as the entire country, and therefore some people would have supposed that all they had to do was to save the cards for these twenty-nine counties, throw away the rest, and tabulate these at any time later to get a picture of the country. Whereupon Gini and Galvani proceeded to make some tabulations to see how closely they would turn out. They discovered—I won't say to their horror, because a scientific man always takes what nature gives him—but they discovered anyhow that in many characteristics other than the original fifteen the sample was no good. It gave terrible results. They showed the results as warnings—don't do this thing!

Yet a lot of market research proceeds by this very thing that should not be done. Only today a commercial research man showed me what he was doing and expressed his disappointment at the results—they don't check out. He was only learning the lesson that Gini and Galvani warned men against. A random sample can be adjusted to controls, but a biased sample cannot be without running desperate risks. How long will it take for this practice to be understood?

Of course I think there is a difference between the expenditure of public funds and of private funds. I think that if a research man and his client get together and want to do a job a certain way, for heaven's sake, it's their money and far be it from me that they shouldn't spend it that way. They may decide on a biased sample such as a selection of a "typical" city or county by personal judgment, and they may use the quota method or mailed questionnaire. In many problems this is the proper approach. It all depends on the problem and the allowable biases. The proper approach is whatever gives the needed information within the accuracy required, at the lowest cost. But when it comes to Government expenditure our clients are awfully hard to satisfy, and we don't know exactly who they are going to be. Every figure is subject to investigation, and we have been pushed to produce figures that we could stand back of.

My remarks all come from that point of view. Dr. Watson said, I think we are getting closer and closer together as the requirements in market research get more and more stringent and more and more information per dollar is demanded. As the requirements tighten up, the need for knowledge of standard errors and biases increases, and it is in those areas that we in the Government have been working.

Nobody takes any greater pleasure in talking to market research people than Mr. Hansen and I do, and we have lots of opportunity, I might add. We are desirous of knowing what the problems are in marketing research and, as Mr. Hansen has pointed out many a time, tremendous savings can be made either in biased or unbiased methods through the application of recent techniques.

Dr. Watson, you said that some of the young people here should take courses in sampling and market research. Will you tell me where they can get such a course?

WATSON: The situation still exists that the student is forced to get statistics in one place and marketing somewhere else, and bring them together himself according to his own application.

DEMING: When it comes to the matter of cheaper methods and biased methods, I am in favor of them when they deliver the accuracy that is required. But we have to know what the accuracy of our survey is; we dare not guess. In my particular job with the Bureau of the Budget we are and should be tremendously concerned with expenditures. Now one of the points I was trying to make this morning is: How are we going to know whether an expenditure is a wise one without knowing what we are going to get for our money? Moreover, we must know in advance what we are going to get. It is now possible, thanks mainly to Mr. Hansen, to buy statistics the way we buy anything else—on a specification basis. We can and must know in advance that certain biases either will not be there or will certainly be reduced to negligible proportions. We can and must know in advance that the sampling tolerance will be so many per cent, and that the plan will cost so much money.

We in the Government are continually looking for possibilities of saving more money; that is why we need more sampling theory and more facilities with which to put that theory to work. So when I say we aim to do a sampling job in the cheapest way possible, I mean cheapest at the present time. Next year it could be done a little cheaper and the next year still cheaper, thanks to continued mathematical research. Sampling practice is continually growing, more theory developing, more facilities being acquired to use the new theory, and the interaction continues.

When it comes to lower cost and the use of cheaper methods, we want to use mail responses, and we do, and anything else that will give more information for the money. However, we are afraid of an incomplete mail response. Some very recent applications have been made of a mail response, supplemented by a face-to-face interview of a subsample of the non-responses for evaluating the mail returns, so that we can tell what we have and thus know what we are getting for our money. Of course the selection of the sample must be a random one in the first place, and that is where our practice starts to depart from the usual practice in market research.

So, while I think our standards may be different, at least for a while, we are striving toward the same thing. All of us are trying to get information the cheapest way possible. We have many of the same problems to which similar researches and methods are applicable, and that is why I welcome this opportunity of getting together and taking back with me some new ideas to apply in sampling.

One last point: I think it is highly desirable for market research people to keep ahead of their clients, and that it would be detrimental to all statistical work if this were not done. If public confidence in statistics is destroyed, we all suffer. We must all therefore make every effort to keep ahead in techniques, develop them, find out what is happening, and learn how to understand and apply them.

Now that isn't easy to do. There are lots of barriers in the way, but I agree with Dr. Watson that it is going to be done. A lot of progress has been made in the last few years in coöperation, and more will be made. I think some of the methods that have been used in market research have been plenty good enough in the past and therefore have been the proper ones to use; but maybe today we ought to keep our eyes open to the future. How do the requirements change? Will the standards be the same three or five years from now? Think of the different problems in market research and public opinion that are crying for solution today and demanding extremely careful quantitative work, perhaps beyond the limitations of any organization to carry out as matters stand now. There are avenues that are not being explored, but somebody is going to open them up some day.

DISCUSSION

HANSEN: I'd like to summarize with a few remarks and see if there are not some questions and discussion among the panel members and then perhaps discussion from the floor.

Just a remark or two at the outset. I'd like to make a suggestion, because I think a great deal of confusion has arisen in the discussion about area sampling and quota sampling particularly, and other sampling methods also. I believe a lot of confusion arises out of the terminology alone in such discussion. I know plenty of instances where people use area-sampling methods that do not produce results wherein you can measure the precision of the results from the survey itself, because the survey is based on a purposive sample. One such purposive method is the popular quota-sampling method. There are many sampling procedures other than area sampling in which you can measure the precision of the results of the survey from sample results themselves; therefore it seems to me that it is desirable to put a little different emphasis on terminology. I think it is true that people who have been using area-sampling methods a good deal have also been talking about measurability of results, accomplished by methods other than empirical comparisons with known data, which is the term I would like to use. It is whether or not a sample method produces results the precision of which can be measured or evaluated objectively that is the important distinction, rather than whether the method is area sampling or not. The approach to measurability, as I am using it, refers to the situation whereby you can evaluate the precision of results from the sample itself without any assumption that if this sample represents one item therefore it represents another item. I think that a good deal of clarity would come out of a change of terminology. We often see methods used that are not area-sampling methods but do provide objective measurability, and we often find area methods that do not, and I think the terminology that distinguishes between area and other methods lends confusion. That's just an effort to clarify the issue in this field.

I think we have been presented here with a sort of dilemma by the speakers thus far. It is very easy for some of us to be virtuous when we talk, and say that we want to use modern methods of sampling, methods for which we can measure the precision of results, methods for which we shall get the most information per dollar expended.

But if I understand Mr. Barton, he was saying that those methods are all very good in their place and they have places, but they won't work in our place. They won't work for the job we have got to do because we can't predesignate a group of people and get interviews from them, or at least get continuing interviews from them. Now if this may be true of the type of design that he's working with, it seems to me there is a dilemma presented. If the methods won't work when we start to put them in practice, either we have a group of problems for which we have got to find improved methods that will work, or work with existing methods to obtain what I would like to call a scientific approach to minimizing error. You must find an intuitive approach if you cannot measure the errors themselves, in order to accomplish reduction of sampling error and increased production per dollar.

POLITZ: I don't want to interrupt the train of thought that has just been introduced; what has been brought up is important. But it occurred to me that it might be worth while to call attention to one problem which I see so many people worrying about nowadays. That is the problem of weighting. I hear so frequently that someone is going to "weight" something, and I am inclined to be afraid of many of the procedures applied to weighting and the principle involved in it.

This all goes back to the problem of the use of judgment. I'm sure there need not be anything wrong in using judgment. If we use judgment for setting up strata, I think we are completely on safe ground. If we are wrong in anticipating that a certain characteristic which we use as a base for stratification is unimportant to the problem, we still cannot do any harm. We made a wrong guess, to be sure, but this guess doesn't affect the accuracy of the results. Whereas in the case of the other type of judgment in area sampling, I think as much judgment is permitted in this particular case, but it definitely must be forbidden when it refers to the individual respondent or individual city or individual group or population. It seems to me there is a lot of confusion connected with this point. Once we are willing to permit judgment, some people will inevitably use it in areas where it is *not* permitted. I would like to offer a sort of formula for the use of judgment subject to correction and refinement, and say *judgment which we can use for stratification is all right.* If the judgment is wrong it doesn't affect the result, it doesn't create any biases, it only lowers the efficiency. But *judgment in reference to the individual respondent or area or group has to be removed.*

Now, all this has a bearing on the problem which I brought up originally, that is the problem of weighting. In the case of weighting I feel that judgment is often the source of danger. For instance, some people discover after the survey has been made, on the basis of a comparison with some known characteristics, that, for instance, the given sample is wrong on education when they compare education on the basis of the information the census has supplied. Suppose now we can believe that the census information is right, and we conclude that the survey provides us with information that differs with reference to education. We say the survey wasn't done for the purpose of measuring education. We don't worry about the difference or else we say we'll remove the difference by weighting. So if we now are out of line with education and remove education merely by weighting the survey, then we must be "right" on what we actually did the study for. To me the whole procedure seems very dangerous and again goes back to a certain confusion.

Let me introduce an example to show why this kind of weighting need not get us the right result. Let's say we are biased in a survey. We want to find out how often people go to the movies. It so happens that for the convenience of the interviewers most of the interviews are being taken in the environs of the city because the response is easier; people are more often at home, and there are single houses which are easier to approach. Now at the end of the survey the statisticians find out from some other tests that the number of children in the families has something to do with the frequency of going to the movies. Women who have a lot of children cannot go to the movies as often as other women do. Therefore someone may guess that the number of children is related to the frequency of going to the movies.

But now we check the survey, and find that there are more children in the sample than in the universe. If someone says "Let's weight it back," I think this kind of weighting is dangerous. Our interviewer didn't look for people with more children; we didn't distort the sample purposely. It so happened that when we decided to go out of the city we went into neighborhoods where there are more children; and if we weight back, in spite of the fact that children have something to do with going to the movies, we don't necessarily remove the bias in regard to going to the movies: those people living outside the city can't go as often because there aren't any movies.

That's an example that came up in my mind as we were going on with the discussion here; therefore I was wondering if we can arrive at some kind of practical formula which in one respect is scientific, in other respects even reflects on the ethics of our profession: *Whoever dares to use too much of his judgment behaves unscientifically.* He already believes that his theories must be the right ones, whereas real scientific behavior is willing to be modest. Can we perhaps arrive at this formula: *Don't weight anything.* Don't try to move anything back by weighting. If you yourself caused the distortion in the beginning, then it's all right by weighting it back because you know the cause of it. In this way cause and removal is on the same scale.

For instance, take New York's five boroughs, and one borough in Staten Island with fewer people. If you just go over all samples of New York, then the number of cases in Staten Island is so small that later on in a breakdown you cannot afford to make a statement about Staten Island. But if one part of your purpose is to make a statement about Staten Island as contrasted to Brooklyn, then what you would do is throw a greater proportion of your sample into Staten Island than is established by the true ratio of population. That is, you *overweight* purposely the Staten Island sample, and it is completely proper, if you throw all the results together to make a statement about all New York City, to weight Staten Island back in proportion.

I would say it is both scientific and ethical here. If you dare to weight anything back on a characteristic that you yourself didn't purposely distort, I think science as well as ethics are at stake. So I wonder if this kind of formula in reference to weighting would be acceptable or can be refined.

HANSEN: I think your remarks, Mr. Politz, are relevant to the remarks I made. Let's eliminate judgment in the selection process, which was the view that I interpreted Mr. Barton to say wasn't possible in the work he is doing. You raised an interesting question here. Does someone want to speak on the question?

WATSON: I'd like to separate what I believe are two problems we are talking about. One is the original selection of the families and the area-sampling methods applied to that original selection; the original selection of the doorbells I spoke about. The other is the problem of what to do if the lady does not answer the door, if you get an incomplete interview, etc.

Those are two distinct problems. One is the original selection, the other is what to do in the interviewing situation, and I think Mr. Barton had both in mind; original selection and the very practical problem of what to do when families drop out and create biases. If that is true, then what we have been talking about in the panel is, I believe, a method of selecting originally, and what to do about biases later on. Mr. Barton, do you agree that that is a fundamental expression of our problem?

BARTON: Perhaps unfortunately, I introduced the peculiar case that is represented in the panel type operation because it does involve us in two kinds of discussion. Up to this point I have no argument whatever with any of the things said here except on one little quarrel with Dr. Deming, that the specifications and the needs for measurement and accuracy and so on are the same for private industry as they are for government. Without wanting to get into a discussion of differences between government and industry, certainly all of us have taken the position that we are seeking the measurable results and are seeking them most efficiently.

The only other two points I made seem not in any way to disagree with anything that's been said. First was the citation of a few examples of the difficulties applied in the automatic selection devices; not that that makes them impossible but perhaps statisticians can't recognize the existence of the difficulties, and in the design of the sample tend to minimize them.

I'd just like to add one thing—I think it's generally unappreciated by the statisticians. This is not contributing anything to scientific thought, but it is reporting an existing situation. That is that I believe few statisticians have any concept of the complete and extensive degree of erroneous conclusions that most manufacturers reach on a variety of problems. Their decisions are based on their own sample of experience, their own personal experiences in what happens in their neighborhood A & P store, what their wives tell them, misinterpretations of things that happen in their own personal experiences and, as a practical thing, one of the reasons we have research at all today, and one of the reasons that perhaps 95 per cent of the research is done on a quota basis, is that it is reducing some of the broad area of misconception that exists.

HANSEN: I'd like to pose answers to the two questions that have been raised directly here. The first was raised by Mr. Politz concerning a formula for weighting, that we should not introduce weighting into sample results unless the aspects of the sample design which calls for weighting were purposely introduced in the design, in a shift of probability of selection, I presume.

I would like to suggest that there are two circumstances, one in which the weighting of results is highly desirable and appropriate even though the situation suggested by Mr. Politz does not hold. Just take a simple case for illustration, a random sample of a population. If you know certain characteristics about the population from which you are sampling, you can, by appropriate weighting and adjustment procedures, introduce reduction in sampling variance by making use of the known totals. Obtaining and making use of that information will reduce the sampling errors. When you're dealing with sample errors, I see nothing wrong with those procedures. On the other hand, when you're dealing with purposive samples, since the whole approach is a purposive one, I don't think that there is a scientific answer other than an intuitive one to the question whether you can weight or not. If you're dealing with intuitive approach to the sample without any mathematical model that you are following, then it would seem, if your intuition tells you to weight, that is the thing to do.

I am led to the rejection of the rule that Mr. Politz suggests. You may or may not improve the result by weighting in the intuitive case. One depends on his best judgment, and often an expert's judgment is pretty good and likely to help, but it may not in certain circumstances, as you suggest.

The other question, which I posed myself, I don't think has an easy answer that we can deal with here. That is the question of how to solve the dilemma. While Mr. Barton might get a random sample to start a panel, some might quit, you have to get others to take their place and pretty soon you find yourself in the position that you no longer have a chance selection, that you're working more or less with a purposive sample. I don't think there is any easy answer to this problem. If one wants to insist upon methods that are measurable, I think an answer can be found, but also, if one wants to deal with methods where you can get measurability of results, the cost may be higher than it is worth. If your purposes can be served with judgment methods—and that is what you are reduced to if you cannot use the other methods—you may not be willing to pay the price of getting random methods; but the system of rejection can be solved, and I think there is no reason to assume right now that it need be more expensive. If it is, one would have to examine it. You have two groups in the population, those who will coöperate on the type of approach that is now taken, and those who won't. Pay the price that you now pay for those who do coöperate, and a different approach and somewhat higher price has to be paid to get a higher degree of coöperation from the others. Ways of getting that coöperation can be found, and because you don't have to deal with all of them it may be the way of getting the most information per dollar, even though not getting the most cases per dollar.

I'd like to ask if there are questions or comments from the audience. STEPHAN: I have two things to say: (1) Perhaps we are exaggerating a little when we put this up as a dilemma. There are not two methods; there is a great spectrum of methods with many variations, so that it would be a disservice to the consumer of these studies if he believes that if he has an area sample he has the best that can be provided. That is a fallacious statement if taken as a philosophical statement to be applied in all instances.

(2) I think we tend to overlook the importance of other types of improvement besides the improvement of the sampling design; we must also consider simultaneously the possibilities of improving the other stages in the process of getting the information and applying it, along with the choices that may have to be made about the method of sampling. The method of sampling is very accurate when applied with the method of interviewing or methods of applying the results of the interview with the probable method of action. But it's just like trying to use a surgeon's scalpel in a butcher shop, and therefore I think that the statisticians and market research men are going to be thrown off more and more into methods of getting the information and linking up those improvements with the improvements in the methods of getting samples.

APPLICATION OF MEASUREMENT OF ATTITUDES

PARTICIPANTS

CHAIRMAN: Russell L. Ackoff, *Department of Philosophy, University of Pennsylvania.* SPEAKERS: Morris S. Viteles, *Department of Psychology, University of Pennsylvania;* Dorwin Cartwright, *Department of Psychology, Massachusetts Institute of Technology*

THE MEASUREMENT OF EMPLOYEE ATTITUDES
By
MORRIS S. VITELES

THE most significant development in industrial psychology during the past decade is the growing concern of industrial psychologists with the sentiments, feelings, and attitudes of workers, supervisors, and managers, and with the interplay of people in the social organization of the industrial enterprise. This development parallels a growing recognition on the part of industrial executives that their ordinary channels of communication often fail to provide a clear picture of what is on the worker's mind as a basis for the formulation and administration of personnel policies and practices.

It has become increasingly apparent to management that the avowed, and even actively administered, policy of the "executive open door" has failed to reveal widespread and deep-seated employee grievances. There is growing disinclination to rely upon the reports and interpretations of employee attitudes provided by supervisors and foremen, who are seldom in a key position for obtaining representative and unbiased samplings of employee opinions or reporting them accurately. Many executives now freely acknowledge that relatively few managements actually know what their employees want. They know what management *thinks* the employees want. As a result, far-sighted management is making increasing use of employee opinion or attitude surveys to provide itself with a measure of its "own success or failure in personnel matters and at the same time with a map which locates the specific problems of unsatisfactory feelings and sources of irritation where remedial measures are called for. Incidental to these primary purposes, though likewise of great practical importance, the attitude surveys also operate to relieve tensions by letting workers unburden themselves, to improve morale by showing that management is really interested in the people on the job, and to give management valuable concrete case material for use in instructing supervisors." [1]

The usual methods for the assessment of employee opinion are being used in such surveys. Both the guided and unguided interview have been used, as, for example, in the well-known study at the Hawthorne Plant of the Western Electric Company. However, more frequently, by reasons of relative simplicity, objectivity, and economy, use is being made of attitude scales and questionnaires of various types. It seems appropriate, as a background for discussion, to review briefly the methods employed and the results obtained in a few such studies.

The work of Uhrbrock furnishes a classic example [2] of the use of an attitude scale constructed in accordance with the principles formulated by Thurstone.[3] Two hundred and seventy-nine statements, representing a great variety of opinions that employees might have about their company, were sorted by one hundred college professors and graduate students into eleven piles, and the scale value of each item determined by averaging the piles to which it was assigned by the hundred judges. Fifty statements with scale values from 0.6 to 10.5, among them items pertaining to varied company policies and practices, were included in the final "employee attitude" scale. The following illustrates both the types of statements used and their scale values:

Scale
Value
10.4 I think this company treats its employees better than any other company does.
8.9 A man can get ahead in this company if he tries.
8.5 The company is sincere in wanting to know what its employee thinks about it.
5.4 I believe accidents will happen no matter what you do about them.
5.1 The workers put as much over on the company as the company puts over on them.
4.1 Soldiering on the job is increasing.

1 A. W. Kornhauser, "Psychological Studies of Employee Attitudes," *Journal of Consulting Psychology*, 1944, Vol. 8, 127.
2 R. S. Uhrbrock, "Attitudes of 4,430 Employees," *Journal of Social Psychology*, 1934, 5, 365–77.
3 L. L. Thurstone, "Theory of Attitude Measurement," *Psychological Review*, 1929, 36, 222–41.

2.9 My boss gives all the breaks to his lodge and church friends.

2.5 I think the company goes outside to fill good jobs instead of promoting men who are here.

1.5 In the long run this company will "put it over" on you.

1.0 The pay in this company is terrible.

The "attitude scale," with the statements arranged in random order in so far as scale values are concerned, was presented to 3,934 factory employees, 96 clerical workers and 400 foremen in various plants of the company, with appropriate instructions, including the request that the blanks be returned without signatures.

The average scores of each of the three groups of employees and the total distribution of scores are shown in the accompanying chart (Figure 1). Differences among the average scores of the three groups are significant.

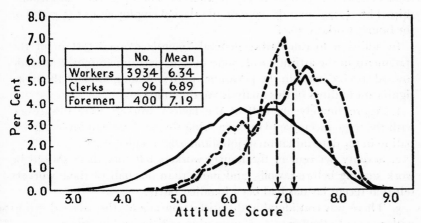

FIG. 1. DISTRIBUTION OF ATTITUDE SCORES OF EMPLOYEES

It is apparent that the average score of factory workers (6.34) is approximately at the midpoint of the scale (6.0) and that the distribution is approximately normal. In contrast, the average score of clerical workers (6.90) and the skewed distribution of measures shows a more "favorable" attitude toward the plant than exists among factory workers. Even more "favorable" is the attitude of foremen with an average score of 7.59, with few scores below 5, and a considerable number of scores at the higher end of the scale.[4]

Such distributions of scale scores are generally accepted as giving an overall picture of what has been commonly designated as employee "morale." From a chart such as that shown, it would be generally con-

[4] The survey also revealed differences among several of the plants which are not discussed in this paper.

cluded that, in the plants under consideration, the morale of foremen and clerical employees was generally favorable, whereas specific items of dissatisfaction were tending to lower the overall "morale" of factory workers.

A step generally taken in making practical use of such attitude surveys is that of identifying the specific factors which account for low morale scores. Bergen,[5] for example, reports on the use of a questionnaire involving a combination of an "attitude scale" with questions of the multiple type, employed in measuring the "morale" and reactions to particular policies of 1,000 employees from selected office and factory departments of a manufacturing company. Results showed a range in average departmental morale scores from 45.9 to 69.4 with an average of 57.1 for all employees. A further analysis revealed that these variations in morale were due largely to differences in supervision and leadership. The average morale score of all salaried employees was 57.5 and of the hourly workers, 56.0.

In addition to calculating general "morale scores," certain of the statements in the attitude scale were used to measure employee attitude toward specific items in the personnel policy. Among some of the more significant findings of this analysis are the following:

1. Approximately one-half of the factory workers were dissatisfied with the wage incentive plan, suggesting the need for employee participation in the determination of job standards and piece rates.

2. Seventy per cent of the hourly workers felt that there should be work sharing before lay-offs, and more than one-half of these workers felt that recent lay-offs had been handled fairly.

3. There was considerable dissatisfaction among the salaried group with respect to the fairness of promotion policies and practices.

4. Twenty-eight per cent of the factory employees were convinced that the company employed labor spies, although this was not the case.

5. A close relationship appeared between departmental morale and attitudes toward supervision and leadership.

The findings of many such surveys have focused attention upon the quality of supervision as a prime factor in determining the level of employee satisfaction or morale. Typical are the outcomes of a survey conducted during 1940 by the Florida Power and Light Company.[6] In this experiment all the employees of the Miami Branch of this utility were

[5] H. B. Bergen, "Finding Out What Employees are Thinking," *Ind. Conf. Board Management Record*, April 1939, 1–6.

[6] McG. Smith, "Mending our Weakest Links," *Advanced Management*, 1942, 7, 77–83.

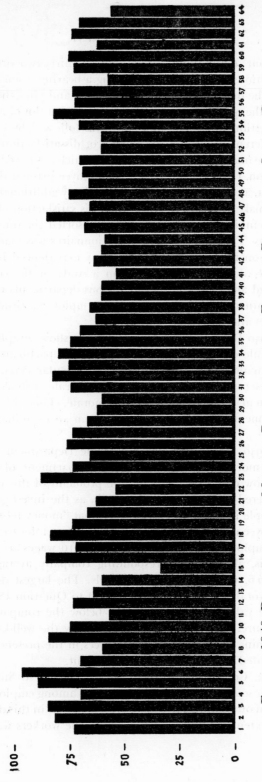

Fig. 2. 1940 Departmental Morale Profile in the Florida Power and Light Company

asked to fill out a questionnaire containing thirty-two questions on working conditions in the company having a bearing upon employees' satisfaction. The questionnaires were unsigned, and after the employee had filled out the questionnaire he dropped it into a slot of a large steel box. Each question in the questionnaire was followed by five answers expressing different degrees of satisfaction or dissatisfaction. Each person checked the one answer to each question which expressed his feeling on that question. On the front page the employee printed the name of his department, and on the back page printed any additional comments he wished to make having a bearing upon his satisfaction on the job.

A special committee of a dozen employees sorted the questionnaires by departments. The analysis of the questionnaires was made by a disinterested person from outside the company experienced in this type of work and centered particularly upon a study of the comparative "morale" found among employees in various departments of the company as determined from the expressions of employee attitudes towards various policies and practices.

Figure 2, 1940 Departmental Morale Profile, shows graphically how much the morale of this company varied from department to department. Each bar on the chart represents a particular department, the long bar represents a department with high morale, a short bar stands for a department with a relatively low morale. The wide variations among departments are easily noticeable from an examination of the chart.

Figure 3, 1940 Morale Profile of a Single Department, shows the analysis of the morale situation in one of the departments of this utility. The results show clearly that the morale problems of this department were not centered around wages, although, as the investigator points out, many people in the company assumed that "money tells the whole story of employee morale." Questions 23, 24, and 25 refer to wages. The attitudes of employees in this department toward wages are all "in the black," that is, above the corresponding company averages by the amounts of 10.6, 12.6, and 6.5, respectively. The largest deviation in terms of unfavorable attitude is with respect to Question 18, Criticism in Public; the value in this case is 18.2 below the company average. This item is purely one of leadership. Evidently the well-known principle of refraining from criticizing employees in the presence of others had been violated flagrantly in this department.

Question 13, Consideration and Courtesy Shown to Subordinates, reveals another source of unfavorable attitudes among employees in this department. In other words, the survey revealed that in this department, and to some extent the company as a whole, the workers wanted more

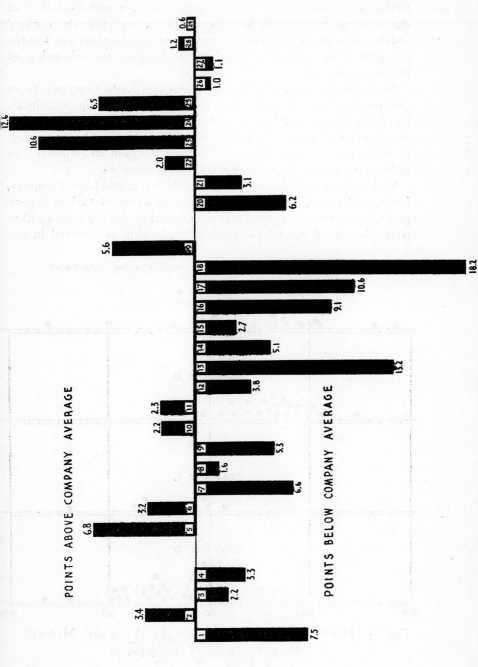

Fig. 3. 1940 Morale Profile of a Single Department in Florida Power & Light Co.

consideration, better treatment by the supervisory force. Such dissatisfaction as existed was not with the wage plan, but with the failure of
the department head and his subordinates to recognize the workers'
worth as human beings. The primary source of dissatisfaction was the
disregard of the workers' feelings and sentiments—the mainsprings of
human conduct.

Such findings led, in the Florida Power and Light Company, to an
extended program of supervisor training in leadership techniques,
based in part upon replies by members of the executive and supervisory
staff to a special questionnaire on leadership problems. This, in passing,
is an illustration of the way in which the findings of an employee attitude survey are put to use by progressive management.

Such surveys, as in the case of the Florida Power and Light Company,
frequently include a comparison of morale scores of various departments in the same company. The accompanying chart (Figure 4), illustrates the spread from department to department as observed in one

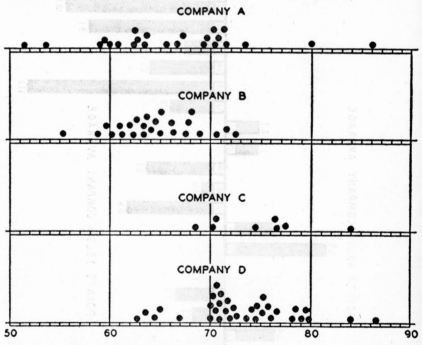

FIG. 4. HOW DEPARTMENTS VARY IN AVERAGE MORALE
SCORES—FOUR COMPANIES

study of four organizations. It can be seen that the variations from department to department within a single company are far greater than
the differences in average morale scores among the four companies.
"The spread in Company A is particularly marked. As a whole, Company A scores somewhat higher than does Company B, yet there appears to be a relatively higher degree of consistency in personnel administration and practices in Company B, since its department scores
cluster more closely about the average." [7] It is interesting to note that
the spread is here also accounted for by differences in the personality
and ability of the executives and managers who have direct supervision
of the several departments. According to the investigator, "employees
who are fortunate enough to be assigned to departments or activities
supervised by executives skilled in the art of 'handling' people can be
expected to have high morale scores. Those less fortunate people who
have to spend their working lives under the boss who is not a good
personnel man or woman are not to be censured if they develop unfavorable attitudes toward the job and the company." [8]

Among other interesting comparisons frequently made in attitude
surveys are those involving employees with varying years of service with
the company. Figure 5 illustrates the results of such an analysis in one
company. Of particular interest is the progressive decrease in morale
with increasing length of service and the contrasting increase in morale
with increasing chronological age within the separate length-of-service
brackets.[9]

It has been suggested that the decrease in morale with increasing
length of service during the first five or ten years, which has been recorded in a number of studies, "is probably a process of disillusionment
involved in the average worker's adjustment to the job." According to
this explanation, the worker "is filled with enthusiasm at first, the job
is more interesting because it is new, he is learning something every
day and can see his productivity increase as he learns, his hopes may
be high. Perhaps this sense of achievement is lessened after the early
period of easy progress is past; certainly there is no opportunity for all
ambitious or hopeful newcomers to get ahead as fast as they may at
first hope."

It has likewise been suggested that "employees who remain on the
payroll for more than five or ten years are a selected group having sur-
vived the constant process of elimination through dismissal or resigna-

[7] R. L. Hull, "Measuring Employee Attitudes—A Proving Ground for Personnel
Policy and Practices." *Conference Board Management Record*, November 1939.
[8] *Ibid.*
[9] *Ibid.*

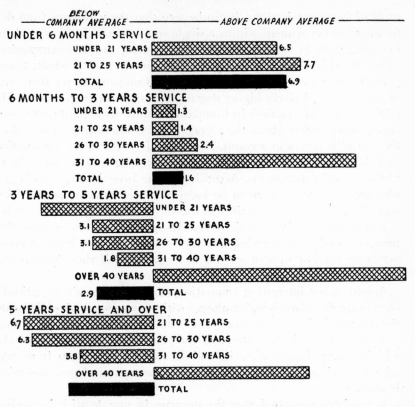

FIG. 5. MORALE SCORES BY AGE GROUPS WITH LENGTH
OF SERVICE HELD CONSTANT

tion. If they are of outstanding ability, that ability may have been recognized. Those who have not advanced have accepted the fact that there is not room at the top for all and have perhaps resigned themselves to their fate, a fate which does not seem so bad after all." [10]

From such studies, involving in most instances a comparison of the average morale scores of groups expressing satisfaction or dissatisfaction with specific items, long lists of influences affecting morale have been compiled. In addition to supervision and length of service, to which reference has been made, wages, job security, sex, hours, conditions of work and surroundings, opportunities for advancement, social relationships on the job, prompt and fair settlement of grievances, etc., have been found of importance in determining employee morale.[11]

[10] *Ibid.*
[11] Kornhauser, *op. cit.*, p. 133.

As suggested by Kornhauser, the wide use of attitude studies is some indication that management is finding the materials of value. As he points out, "findings almost always add substantially to management's previous information about its employees and very often contain startling surprises. Perhaps the greatest accomplishments have been in the way management is shocked out of its complacency with respect to employee satisfaction. Even where the results at first seem dubious to managers, further detailed inquiry into the situation usually reveals some genuine basis for the feelings expressed in the survey—a basis either in the objective conditions or in the subjective meanings these situations have been permitted to assume." [12]

A recent publication [13] lists seven major results from continued employee attitude surveys in one company as follows:

1. They have provided measurements of the trends of employee thought and knowledge about the company, indicating the strengths and weaknesses in the company's program of closer relationship.
2. They have increased the pride and confidence of the employee in his company.
3. They have stimulated suggestions on the part of employees for more improvement.
4. They have strengthened training programs.
5. They have put supervision "on its toes."
6. They have helped management and union to know one another better and to appreciate the fact that the other group is just as desirous of building a sounder industrial commonwealth.
7. They have produced better working conditions. Not only do these spell greater efficiency, but by removing a major cause they lessen the possibility of strikes and costly slow-downs.

In spite of such enthusiastic recognition of the value of employee-attitude surveys, there nevertheless remain troublesome problems with respect to the interpretation and use of survey results both at the company and at the country-wide level. The nature and seriousness of such difficulties may be illustrated by a consideration of conclusions drawn from attitude surveys concerning influence of wages in inducing employee satisfaction and coöperation. The conclusion drawn from many, if not most, of the surveys conducted in the past ten years is that undue stress has been placed upon wages as a factor influencing employee morale. There is a striking degree of agreement on this among investigators using different methods and approaching the problem of employee attitudes from extremely divergent viewpoints.

According to Hull, in a report issued by the Industrial Conference

12 *Ibid.*, p. 130.
13 "Sampling Workers' Opinions." *Dun's Review*, November 1945.

Board, "results from a series of studies suggest that employers and labor leaders alike have concentrated their attention on the tangibles of the employer-employee relationships to the neglect of equally important intangibles. Giving the worker more pay for fewer hours of work is a spectacular accomplishment. Giving him courteous and considered treatment, competent instruction, and the respect due him as an individual may be less spectacular but will bring dividends of loyalty and coöperation which cannot be bought. Man does not live by bread alone." [14]

As indicated earlier in this discussion, one conclusion drawn from the study made by the Florida Power and Light Company is that "the chart (Figure 3) shows definitely that the morale problems of this department are not wages, although many people blandly assume that money tells the whole story of employee morale." [15]

On the basis of attitude surveys involving one hundred thousand workers in large corporations, Houser, who pioneered in this field of employee-attitude surveys, placed the likelihood of pay increases from time to time "as the last of importance in a series of twelve factors which employees, including unskilled labor, but not including sales personnel, said mattered most to them."

According to Goodwin Watson,[16] the rank assigned to various factors in morale by several hundred employers and three thousand employees surveyed by the National Retail Drygoods Association is that shown in Table 1, with fair pay ranked third by employees and first by employers. Watson also reports on studies conducted in coöperation with Seidman, in which high-school graduates seeking employment, and workers, gave reasons for their preferences for one job as compared with another. The results, presented in Tables 2 and 3, lead to the statement that "the findings again point to the importance of recognition, friendly association, and variety of work which seem to be of greater concern than wages or hours." A note of caution is introduced by the investigator, who points out that "the income from the preferred job was actually greater than the earnings in four out of five of the other jobs held" (in the case of the workers), but he goes on to point out that "the report of the workers was that the difference in money was not the major consideration."

Viewing the situation from a broader philosophical position, Whitehead of Harvard University has gone so far as to insist, largely on the

14 Hull, *op. cit.*
15 Smith, *op. cit.*
16 G. Watson, "Work Satisfaction," in *Industrial Conflict—A Psychological Interpretation.* New York, The Gordon Company, 1939, 114-24.

TABLE 1

RANK ASSIGNED VARIOUS FACTORS IN MORALE BY EMPLOYERS AND EMPLOYEES

Morale Item	Employee Ranking	Employer Ranking
Credit for all work done	1	7
Interesting work	2	3
Fair pay	3	1
Understanding and appreciation	4	5
Counsel on personal problems	5	8
Promotion on merit	6	4
Good physical working conditions	7	6
Job security	8	2

(After Watson)

TABLE 2

REASONS ASSIGNED BY 157 YOUNG MEN, HIGH SCHOOL GRADUATES, FOR PREFERRING ONE JOB RATHER THAN ANOTHER

Reason	Per Cent
1. In line with vocational aspirations	29
2. Congenial contacts with people	24
3. Like responsibility, chance to use initiative, prestige	19
4. Variety	12
5. Opportunity for promotion	8
6. Salary better	4
7. Shorter hours	4
	100

(After Watson)

TABLE 3

REASONS ASSIGNED BY 100 WORKERS FOR PREFERRING ONE JOB RATHER THAN ANOTHER

Reason	Per Cent Men	Women
1. Congenial working conditions, pleasant social contacts	21	38
2. Responsibility, initiative, prestige	27	23
3. In line with vocational aspiration	15	13
4. More variety	15	12
5. More salary	13	6
6. Better chance for promotion	6	2
7. Shorter hours	3	6
	100	100

(After Watson)

basis of results from the Hawthorne experiment, that the basic psychological generalization of economics, as applied in industry, "has exhausted much of its usefulness at the present time" and "has become a positive danger to our social and economic structure. By postulating men and women as actuated in their economic activities solely by a desire for personal gain," he writes, "attention has been so far diverted from a due consideration of the social motives involved that these are being systematically thwarted in our present economic civilization. We need," he adds, "to develop an organic conception of society in which economic activities take their place as one important aspect of the whole social process." [17]

The statements cited are representative of many similar conclusions reported during the past ten years. The factor in the situation which concerns me at the moment is that the workers themselves have apparently not heard the results of such surveys and the conclusions because, in spite of the repeated occurrence of emphasis on the relative unimportance of pay, the demand for higher wages still appears as the basic, and in some instances the only, demand in a great majority of the strikes which have troubled our country during the past ten years and which are besetting this country today.

Many explanations of this situation can and have been suggested. It may be said that statements concerning the relative importance of factors other than pay are correct, but that the present wage-price relationship, and that existing throughout the war, have tended to place wages in the foreground of workers' demands.

It is commonly recognized, too, that employee-attitude surveys are generally conducted only in better plants since executives hesitate to undertake such surveys when they are "sitting on a powder keg." It may be that such plants pay better wages, and that the attitude survey reveals what is actually the case in spite of the country-wide strike situation.

Another explanation frequently given is that demands for higher pay really conceal other sources of dissatisfaction. Bergen has phrased this colorfully in the statement: "Of course, all employees want 'more money.' Who doesn't? But they want good leadership and efficient management much more. These demands they cannot always discuss tangibly. Consequently, employees' discontent takes the form of demands for higher pay because this is something they talk about to management, either individually or through union committeemen." [18]

The same viewpoint is emphasized by Watson in the statement that "without in any way denying the need of many workers for higher

[17] T. N. Whitehead, "Social Motives in Economic Activities," *Occup. Psychol.*, 1938, 12, 273 f.

[18] H. B. Bergen, "Measuring Wartime Attitudes and Morale," *Personnel Journal*, 1942, 21, 2–9.

wages, it may be recognized that sometimes workers, vaguely dissatisfied with the way things are going, know no other way of meeting the situation. They ask for more pay or shorter hours, and perhaps they should have these, but if these demands were attained, the relief would be only temporary. *The underlying cause of dissatisfaction may be not in the pay envelope or the time clock, but in the work itself.*" [19]

The contradiction between "opinion" and "fact" may arise from inadequacies in the survey methods themselves. In a most thoughtful review of employee-attitude measurement recently published by Kornhauser,[20] attention is drawn to difficulties in survey methods and in the interpretation of results which require careful consideration in this connection. As he points out, "superficial and misleading conclusions flow too easily from the mere inspection of simple correlation figures or percentage comparisons of groups"—certain of the methods lead "to the fallacy of imputing direct causal influence to a correlated variable which may be only an incidental accompaniment of the actual determinance." Others, involving a direct rating of the relative importance of job attributes may lose practical significance "since the abstract characteristics have varied meanings for the employees, and especially because the ratings turn so largely upon unanalyzed assumptions, in the rater's mind, as to the range of variations in each of the variables under consideration."

Any or all of these explanations may be correct in part or in whole. Nevertheless all of them fail to suggest what may be the basic requirement in the situation, namely, that the discovery of definitive data on factors underlying employee morale requires something more than the attitude survey. There is a real danger that the extensive use of employee-attitude surveys, and the favorable outcomes of such surveys in reducing industrial conflict, are blinding both the business man and the psychologist—and most particularly the latter—to the need for another approach, primarily that of direct experimentation—or what Kornhauser calls the "true experiment" as a "source of more reliable information on the importance of specific factors in determining employee morale."

The nature and possibilities of such experimentation can perhaps be illustrated in a study of wage incentives conducted in England by Wyatt, Frost, and Stock.[21] This involved a comparison of the effects of *time rate, bonus rate,* and *piece rate* systems of wage payment on the output

[19] Watson, *op. cit.*, p. 115.
[20] Kornhauser, *op. cit.*, 140 ff.
[21] S. Wyatt, L. Frost, and F. G. L. Stock, *Incentives in Repetitive Work,* Ind. Health Res. Bd. Report No. 69, London, 1934.

and feelings of workers engaged in the repetitive tasks of wrapping; weighing and wrapping; packing, weighing, and unwrapping, respectively. As can be seen from the chart (Figure 6), the substitution of a bonus rate for a time rate increased average output 46%. A further increase of 30% in average production was obtained when the bonus rate was replaced by a piece rate.

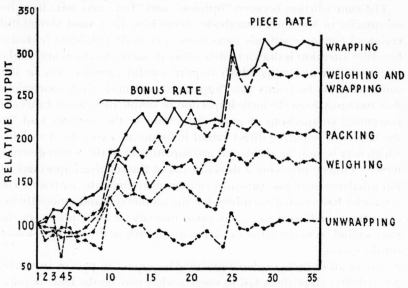

Fig. 6. Relative Output in Successive Weeks in Different Processes under the Influence of Various Wage-payment Plans

Each worker was employed on each of the five tasks. In the course of the experiment, the order of *worker preference* for the tasks was determined by means of guided interviews. The order preference proved to be: (1) *wrapping*, (2) *weighing* and *wrapping*, (3) *packing*, (4) *weighing*, (5) *unwrapping*. As can be seen from the chart presented as Figure 6, on the most preferred task, *wrapping*, the rate of output was almost trebled by the end of the experiment while production on the least-preferred task, *unwrapping*, remained completely unaffected by any of the wage-incentive payment plans. The interviews led investigators to the conclusion that if an operation is regarded as totally aimless and futile, the strongest monetary incentive may have no effect in improving output.

The experiment is of interest in illustrating the manner in which conclusions concerning specific factors can be enriched through direct, controlled experimentation. It indicates the extent to which the errors that accrue from generalizations made on assumptions concerning the inter-action of variables, as is frequently the case in attitude surveys, can be avoided by an analysis involving the examination of single variables considered separately in accord with an appropriate experimental design.

As indicated earlier, many of the employee-attitude surveys have led to the opinion that supervision is the most single important factor in the determination of employee morale. However, in few cases has the situation been examined experimentally under the controlled conditions such as those appearing in a study described by Feldman,[22] relating to the effect of changes in supervision upon production.

Among the employees of an insurance company were approximately a thousand clerks, divided into twenty-two sections. In 1933, a new wage plan providing group incentives for the twenty-two sections was in-augurated. Costs for each section for the previous twelve months were computed and each was allowed a group bonus on the savings it could effect over the cost for that period. All members of a section, including the supervisor, shared in these savings monthly on the basis of salaries, no change being made either in the basic salary or in established policies with respect to salary increases. At the end of 1933, every section showed some improvement, but the extent of improvement for the sections ranged from 2 per cent to 12 per cent with an average of 8 per cent.

In 1934 management effected a general shift of all section heads, with the general aim of putting those who had been in charge of above-the-average bonus groups into those less-than-the-average sections. One objective in this was to determine whether differences in results were related primarily to differences in supervision or to differences in personnel or conditions of work. An analysis of production at the beginning of 1935 showed increases in production in all sections, ranging from 6 per cent to 18 per cent. The order of merit of supervisors remained practically the same as in the study made at the end of 1933. In spite of the reassignment to new sections, those whose units stood high at the end of the first year were at the top of the list during the second year and vice versa. Changes in relative order were limited to three cases of supervisors who had moved a step or two in terms of rank order.

Early in 1935, management again shifted, by lot, twenty of the twenty-two supervisors. Although they were reassigned by chance, the listing at the end of the year showed the surprising result that in progress made the same general order of supervisors again prevailed. Moreover, an analysis of errors in terms of 1935 and 1936 earning records showed

[22] H. Feldman, *Problems in Labor Relations*, New York, The Macmillan Company, 1937.

perfect correlation between the standing of the accuracy record of the work of each section under a supervisor and the standing on the earning record.

Here the conclusions are reached not on the basis of generalizations from surveys involving a multiplicity of factors and an indirect method of analysis, but are the outcomes of a direct experimental change of a single experiment variable. Findings from such experiments merely accentuate the need for insisting upon an opportunity to apply the same rigid experimental controls to studies of factors influencing morale, and in the area of the related variable of employee performance, as are insisted upon in investigations conducted by psychologists in other areas. It is recognized that such studies, as Kornhauser suggests, may of necessity be limited to "specific and narrowly restricted work situations," and that there are many practical difficulties to be overcome in conducting such experiments. Nevertheless the existence of difficulties should be no excuse for lowering standards but rather a challenge to overcome the difficulties in the interest of arriving at explanations, interpretations, and principles based upon accurate and adequate experimental observation." [23]

Pending the accumulation of such experimental evidence on a large scale, there still remains the problem of clarifying the situation with respect to the use of employee-attitude survey data. It is suggested that the situation can be improved by supplying more information concerning individual surveys to those who are concerned with the use of their results and by specifying more clearly the limitations of generalization from survey data.

A striking example of the basic problem is to be found in the conclusions from two studies published almost simultaneously (January 1946)—in this instance by the same research organization. Both of them take up the problem of productivity of the worker and attempt to find out what the workers think about their responsibilities for maintaining production to the best of their ability. The conclusions reached in the two surveys are as follows:

According to the first: *"The worker isn't sure that employees should work as hard as they can and he is sometimes suspicious of management's motives in raising output."* [24]

The conclusion of the second: *"Though he believes in 'protection' of his wage standards, the worker knows that restraints on production are morally wrong."* [25]

[23] M. S. Viteles, "Postlude: The Past and Future of Industrial Psychology." *Journal of Consulting Psychology*, Vol. 8, 1944, 183.

[24] "What the Worker Really Thinks," *Factory Management and Maintenance*, January, 1946.

[25] Confidential Report.

There seems reason for the opinion that the lay reader—if not the expert—will consider these statements as contradictory (certainly as not representing the same *direction* of feeling) and that he may be much disturbed if both should reach his desk simultaneously at a time when he is much concerned with the problem of establishing policies designed to stimulate productivity.

When an examination is made of the questions upon which these generalizations are based, additional light is of course thrown on the apparent discrepancy between them. The first generalization, *"The worker isn't sure that employees should work as hard as they can and he is sometimes suspicious of management's motives in raising output,"* grows out of a series of questions and answers shown in the charts (Figures 7, 8, and 9). It is to be noted that one of the questions asked bears upon the question of loafing, and the conclusion reached that *"All types of employees frown, however, upon 'loafing.'"*

This examination of materials following the leading generalization brings the evaluation of employee attitude closer to the generalization reached in the second of the surveys to the effect that *"Though he believes in 'protection' of his wage standards, the worker knows that restraints on production are morally wrong."* In passing, it may be pointed out that this latter generalization is derived from a question, *"Do you think it is all right for the workers in a gang to get together and agree to turn out only so much in a day, even though some of them could turn out more?"* to which approximately 62 per cent of workers replied, "It is wrong," and approximately 31 per cent, "It is all right." (Figure 10).

Presented with both sets of data, and having both the urge and the time to examine them closely, the plant manager or company president may discover that the two generalizations are not so far apart as appears from a first reading of the generalizations without reference to the supporting data. However, most busy executives have neither the time nor, I suspect, the inclination to engage in such an extended analysis of survey reports. Moreover, in many instances one of the reports may come to the attention of the executive and the other may not. Under any circumstances, the policy adopted by the company may prove to be an "accident" of the materials read by the executive or of his interpretation of seemingly conflicting generalizations.

It seems well to inquire briefly how such discrepancies in generalizations occur and how they can be avoided. As was indicated earlier, the generalizations referred to were prepared by the same research organization and actually distributed in the same month. One happened to be the outgrowth of a survey of "Workers' Attitudes Toward Wage Incentives." The other was included in a more extended survey of "What

FIG. 7

1. THE WORKER ISN'T SURE THAT EMPLOYEES SHOULD WORK AS HARD AS THEY CAN . . .

Question: When a man takes a job in a factory, do you think he should turn out as much work as he can, or should he turn out as much, say, as the average man in his group?

Answer:

AS MUCH AS HE CAN — 49%

AVERAGE AMOUNT — 40%

THAT DEPENDS — 8%

NO OPINION — 3%

FIG. 8

. . . AND HE IS SOMETIMES SUSPICIOUS OF MANAGEMENT'S MOTIVES IN RAISING OUTPUT

Question: (addressed only to those who said "average amount"): What do you think would happen if he turned out *more* than the average?

Answer:

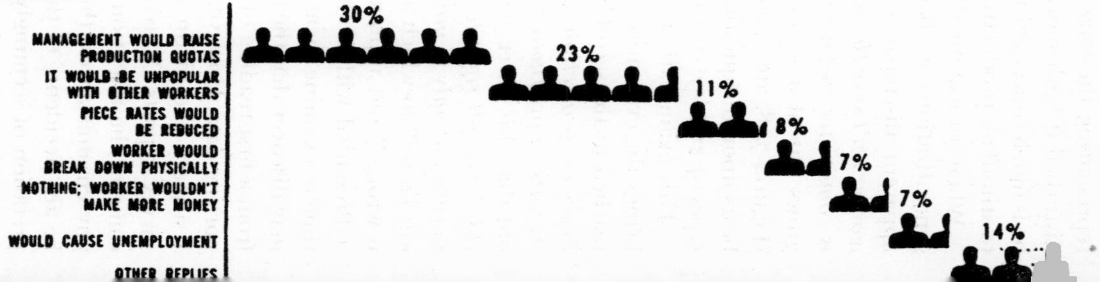

MANAGEMENT WOULD RAISE PRODUCTION QUOTAS — 30%

IT WOULD BE UNPOPULAR WITH OTHER WORKERS — 23%

PIECE RATES WOULD BE REDUCED — 11%

WORKER WOULD BREAK DOWN PHYSICALLY — 8%

NOTHING; WORKER WOULDN'T MAKE MORE MONEY — 7%

WOULD CAUSE UNEMPLOYMENT — 7%

OTHER REPLIES — 14%

FIG. 9. ALL TYPES OF EMPLOYEES FROWN, HOW-EVER, ON "LOAFING"

Question: Here's another idea. There are probably some men in your plant who loaf a little bit. Now suppose nobody loafed and everybody turned out just as much work as he reasonably could—would this help or hurt the workers?

Here are the answers broken down by type of employee:

	Manual Workers	Foremen	Clerical Workers
It would help workers................	61 %	73 %	67 %
It would hurt workers................	11	12	11
It would make no difference..........	11	6	8
That depends......................	7	5	6
No opinion........................	10	4	8

FIG. 10. THOUGH HE BELIEVES IN "PROTECTION" ON HIS WAGE STANDARDS, THE WORKER KNOWS THAT RESTRAINTS ON PRODUCTION ARE MORALLY WRONG

"Do you think it's all right for the workers in a gang to get together and agree to turn out only so much in a day, even though some of them could turn out more?"

	Workers paid by:		
	Hour	Incentive	Piece
It's wrong	62 %	62 %	63 %
It's all right	30	32	29
No opinion	8	6	8

the Factory Worker Really Thinks About Productivity, Nationalization of Industry and Labor, and Politics." Perhaps the differences in the scope of the investigation account for the diversities in generalizations with respect to the same basic issue, in that possibly the general framework of the questions biased both the answers to the questions and, necessarily, the resulting generalizations. It also happens that the one generalization comes from a confidential report, not intended for publication, provided under a service to executives. The other was part of a survey described in full in a magazine read widely by industrial and research personnel. It may be said, without in any way impugning the motives or the integrity of the research organization involved, that this may have been a factor in the phrasing of both the original questions and of the generalization. It is further possible that the variations are accidental in character, associated with the identity of staff members assigned to independent research projects. There is, of course, always the possibility of different population samples, and other sources of variation, although these are matters aside from the present discussion.

From situations of this kind grow questions which are of extreme importance in terms of both conducting and applying the results of attitude surveys. In terms of application, they suggest the need for a somewhat more complete orientation of the reader with respect to the entire frame of reference of the employee-attitude survey; the reasons behind the choice and phrasing of specific questions; the factors in the local and broader scene which may influence the response of the moment; the limiting factors which have and must be considered in the interpretation of findings and in the formation of generalizations. It may well be that experts should tell the laymen, as suggested by Kornhauser, that "valid practical conclusions in this field must be closely akin to clinical judgments regarding total individual personalities or to the balanced administrative decisions of social policy-makers. While scientific procedures contribute useful hints and fragments of evidence which are valuable aids in reaching toward conclusions, this material must always be combined with various other types of information and insight if the conclusions are to become sound practical judgments." [26] In this perhaps rests the immediate future of practical and respectable employee attitude evaluations.

SURVEYS OF THE WAR FINANCE PROGRAM
By
DORWIN CARTWRIGHT [1]

THE purpose of my remarks this afternoon is to give a completely nontechnical description of one approach to the problems associated with predicting and influencing consumer behavior. In order to be specific, this description will take the form of a case study of one large research program undertaken by the Government during the war.

Early in the war, Secretary of the Treasury Morgenthau requested the Division of Program Surveys of the Department of Agriculture to undertake a program of research designed to shed light on the psychological-economic problems of war finance. Through use of sampling and interviewing techniques relatively new at the time, relevant information about public behavior and its motivational, attitudinal, and informational determinants was to be obtained. As the program of public bor-

---

[26] Kornhauser, *op. cit.,* 140.

[1] Dr. Cartwright was a member of the Division of Program Surveys of the Bureau of Agricultural Economics when the research reported here was carried out.

rowing grew, this research was expanded into a continuous service which was intimately integrated with major policy decisions throughout the war.

In about three and one-half years nine major national studies were conducted and twice as many regional or local ones aimed at solving special problems. Moreover, seldom has such large-scale research been integrated so closely with policy formation. Credit for the magnitude of the research program and for its close integration with policy decisions should go to many people, but especially it was the imagination and sensitivity to the possibilities of research on the part of Mr. Morgenthau, Mr. Ted R. Gamble, the War Finance Director, and Dr. Peter Odegard that made these accomplishments possible.

The array of problems investigated during the course of the war is impressive. The Treasury had set for itself the difficult task of raising billions of dollars from the masses of the American people through the sale of Government bonds by voluntary methods. To succeed, it had to organize a publicity and information program unparalleled in history, it had to devise and put into operation new selling techniques, it had to keep the bonds sold since bonds soon redeemed did the Government little good. Research geared to such an administrative program needed to provide information useful in the designing and evaluation of publicity and advertising, including knowledge about effective motives and appeals; it needed to anticipate obstacles to selling, such as the prevalence of fears and rumors detrimental to bonds; it needed to observe closely the factors leading to the successful operation of the Payroll Savings Program; it had to evaluate carefully in detail the strengths and weaknesses of the War Loan Drives; and, finally, it had to provide accurate information concerning the factors producing high or low rates of bond redemptions.

To provide so much information at a time when it would be useful in policy decisions required skillful research planning and organization. Research techniques had to be employed which would yield valid and penetrating findings in an incredibly short period of time. Important variables had to be detected and analyzed while unimportant ones had to be recognized as such and ignored. Research findings had to anticipate conditions which would prevail at a date months in the future. For these reasons we felt it necessary to use techniques which would penetrate deeply into the cognitive and motivational make-up of the American people, which would not provide simply a basis for evaluating past programs but would permit a realistic and scientifically grounded foundation for program planning and development.

Examining more closely the research methods employed, five steps in the procedure may be distinguished. Each step deserves full scrutiny and discussion, but time will permit only a brief sketch here.

1. *Selecting Objectives for a Given Study.* Close coöperation between our research organization and the Treasury policy-makers was essential for the fruitful choice of objectives for a study at any given time. It was necessary to obtain a realistic judgment both of the administrative problems which would be most acute when the results of the study could be made available and of the types of problems which research could best solve. Creative imagination of the highest order was required both in sensing the full possibilities of research and in detecting areas of administration which needed a better scientific grounding. The difference between a successful and unsuccessful research program can be determined in this first step of study planning.

2. *Basic Analysis of Objectives.* After the major objectives of a given project had been agreed upon, it was the task of the research people to work out the research techniques which would best meet the objectives. This job included selecting and describing the population to be studied, the methods of sampling to be followed, the study design (that is, whether contrasting groups are to be compared, whether special informants are to be interviewed, etc.), the particular kind of interview to be used, and the methods of analysis to be employed. In passing, it might be pointed out that all of these surveys were quantitative in the sense defined by Dr. Deming this morning. The selection of the sample, therefore, required consideration of the many points described by Dr. Deming. A most important aspect of the basic analysis was the mapping out of the specific types of information that were needed to satisfy the objectives. In our studies of the War Loan Drives, for example, the objectives seemed to require kinds of information which we grouped under the headings of:

1. Identification of the drive
2. Motivation for buying
3. Implementation for making sales
4. Participation in the drive

Elaborate specifications of data were prepared under each heading. Each of these groups of data was considerably different from the others in the kinds of questions and analysis that it required. Since a central core of the objectives was to determine why people bought or didn't buy in a given drive, much of the basic analysis done in study planning consisted of applying psychological theory to the concrete problems under investigation so that all the variables that promised to be influential could be systematically studied.

3. *The Interview.* The design of the interview schedules used in these studies required the simultaneous fulfillment of several needs. First of all, in order to obtain valid data for a motivational analysis, it was necessary to involve the thoughtful participation of the respondent in the interview; snap answers would not have been desirable. For this reason, considerable attention had to be given to the structural arrangement of the schedule so that interest was aroused and good *rapport* established and maintained. The use of so-called open questions with encouragement for full discussion was found most useful, and questions dealing with matters of personal concern to the respondent were introduced early into the schedule. A second major requirement was that the interview flow naturally from one topic to the next. Although the data covered in a schedule formed a coherent structure from the point of view of those conducting the study, they often seemed unrelated to the respondent. Skill was needed, therefore, in organizing the schedule so that it formed one logical sequence of discussion from the respondent's point of view while satisfying all of the research requirements. The third and most difficult requirement was that questions be designed which would serve as valid indicators of the attitudes, knowledge, motives, and behavior of the respondent which were specified in the basic analysis of the objectives. To guarantee that all of these requirements had actually been met, no study was ever put into operation without a full pre-test and pre-analysis.

In passing, it may be mentioned that a common belief that the Division of Program Surveys always uses the open interview is incorrect. The interview schedules employed in these studies consisted of a whole variety of kinds of questions, the particular type in a given instance being chosen in the light of the requirements just mentioned.

4. *Coding and Analysis.* The conversion of narrative material like that obtained in open questions into quantitative measures of psychological variables is an art whose essential nature no one has yet adequately described. Time does not permit me to make any attempt in this direction here. Certain principles, however, guided our research at this stage. The conversion of the material into quantitative data could be no mechanical procedure to be performed by clerks. The answers had to be classified according to their meaning and significance rather than their mere verbal form. The selection of the *dimensions* of categories was always made in accordance with the demands laid down in the basic analysis of objectives rather than from inspection of the answers obtained in the interviews. One point deserves particular stress. A major asset of the open question is that by producing full discussion it drastically reduces the freedom of interpretation which

the analyst possesses; if properly handled, full narrative answers point to a much narrower range of possible interpretations than any other type of device now used in surveys. After the coding was completed in these studies, the material could then be processed by means of the usual punch-card sort of tabulation. Tabulations and correlations called for by the basic analysis of objectives were then carried forth.

5. *Reporting Findings.* Research people find all too often that the fate of their reports is to gather dust on some busy administrator's desk. Fortunately, in this series of work we avoided this inglorious end. The findings of our research were prepared in a form to be presented in meetings with policy-makers. Charts and slides were prepared. Armed with the facts and means of presenting them vividly, our research people following each study participated in a series of meetings in which their significance for policy was discussed by researchers and practitioners together. Following each study of a War Loan Drive, such discussions were carried on first with the top policy-makers in the Treasury at Washington, then with leaders in the War Advertising Council whose function it was to create the advertising and promotion in future selling, then with the professional staffs of the various sub-divisions of the War Finance Division, and finally with the major volunteer leaders in the state organizations all over the country. The results of these efforts made it abundantly clear that the development of skills of presenting findings is just as important a part of research as the collection and analysis of data.

To give this discussion concrete meaning, let us turn our attention now specifically to the research conducted following each of the War Loan Drives. Rather than describe simply the types of information sought, the major findings will be presented in a highly condensed form.

First, identification of the drives. Several aspects of this problem were investigated. The simplest requirement for success of a drive is that people know of its existence.

Awareness of the Drive. Awareness of the drives has always been at a rather high level. It is interesting, though, that in the first drive conducted for the general public, 19 per cent of the adult population did not realize that there was a special campaign on. In addition, 14 per cent thought of the campaign only as a local drive. That is, they did not know that it was part of a national campaign.

By the fourth drive, awareness had reached a high peak, only 6 per cent of the population being unaware of the drive. This high level was maintained throughout the remainder of the drives.

Understood Purpose of the Drive. In our research we have gone on the assumption that, in order to get full coöperation from the American people, it is necessary for them to understand the reasons or the purposes the Treasury had when setting up a campaign. In line with this, we have attempted to find out from people what they understood the purposes of the drive to be.

In the first public drive it was clear that the effectiveness of the campaign was reduced by the incorrect notions of its purpose held by many of the people who were aware of the drive. It was clear that to many people the drive seemed merely an intensification of the usual sales tactics. Apparently the campaign failed to show them a clear reason for *buying extra during the drive.* The most commonly held view of the purpose of the drive was that it was intended to *remind* people of their obligation to buy bonds. A considerable number of people thought of the drive as being aimed at those who were not yet doing their share. Most people who participated in the payroll deduction plan or who regularly invested at least ten per cent of their income in bonds believed that they were doing their share. They felt, therefore, that the drive was not specifically intended for them. Our recommendation to emphasize the idea of selling extra bonds during a special campaign was taken by the War Advertising Council and made the theme for successive drives so that in the later drives there was no ambiguity about the fact that the bond drives were intended to bring forth extra purchases from the entire population.

Quotas. Closely related to the understood purpose of the drive is the question of how much a person is expected to buy, since the individual quota is a statement of what the Government expects individuals to do in the drive. Prior to the third drive it was evident that people had no clear conception of any specific amount they were expected to buy.

In the Third War Loan Drive an individual quota of a hundred-dollar bond was set.

Although a quota adjusted to individual circumstances might be preferred, the evidence from subsequent surveys was conclusive in demonstrating that the hundred-dollar quota was effective in raising the amount of bonds purchased among large portions of the population. Following the Third Drive, it was found that 20 per cent of the population had heard of the hundred-dollar quota. Approximately a quarter of those who heard about the quota bought at least a hundred-dollar extra bond. On the basis of these findings in the fourth drive, the emphasis upon the quota was more intense, and awareness of the quota increased correspondingly. This time 34 per cent of the population heard of the hundred-dollar quota. Even though more people knew about the quota in the Fourth Drive than in the Third, it is highly important to note that a *larger* proportion of those who heard about it bought at least a hundred-dollar bond. In the Fifth Drive, for a variety of reasons, less stress was put upon the individual quota and fewer people knew about it. Even so, as large a proportion of *those who did hear about it* bought an extra hundred-dollar bond or more. In other words, the quota remained as effective for those who heard of it, but sales were lost because of the fact that the quota was not stressed so much. In the Sixth Drive, emphasis on the quota was increased again, and correspondingly the sale of bonds of larger denominations again increased.

The second major area of investigation covered in each survey deals with motivation for buying bonds. Several approaches were made to this problem. The first was to discover which reasons people would give in answer to several questions directly asking why they bought bonds.

Stated Reasons for Buying Bonds. Three major types of reasons were given by people for buying bonds:

1. Patriotic
2. Personal financial
3. National economic

In interpreting the frequencies of stated reasons it is necessary to realize that the answers people give reflect in great part the things they have been told. For this reason, they are best used to evalute past publicity rather than to design new. Throughout all the surveys it was found that patriotic reasons were given by more people than any other type. Personal financial reasons were given next most frequently, while reasons dealing with the national economy, such as preventing inflation, were given least often.

Effectiveness of Various Reasons. From the point of view of designing future publicity, it is perhaps more important to know which reasons produce results than which reasons are most commonly given. An effort was made in each study to evaluate the effectiveness of various reasons by determining whether or not people who gave them bought more bonds than other people with the same income. On the basis of this analysis, two general types of conclusions were reached following the first public drive:

Only one type of motivation seems to have been particularly effective in inducing people to increase their purchases during the campaign, the investment appeal of bonds. At each income level the investment-minded people, those who spoke of bonds as a good and safe investment, made extra bond purchases during the campaign more than did other groups. The following seem to be the most effective appeals for regular bond buying: prevent inflation, save for some specific postwar use, help a member of the family in the service, save for a postwar depression, invest money safely in bonds.

In succeeding drives essentially the same sort of analysis was conducted with essentially the same results.

A slightly different way of looking at the problem is to ask the question, "Does it make any difference whether people give only one type of reason or more than one type of reason for buying bonds?" The answer to this question has consistently been that it does make a difference. People who see more than one reason for buying bonds are much more apt to buy in drives, whether solicited or not, than those who only have one type of reason. This finding was taken by us as an argument for using more than one type of appeal in war bond drives, but extensive use of this was held back somewhat by the advertising principle that one should plug only one thing at a time.

Plans for Using Money Invested in Bonds. In utilizing personal motivation for selling bonds, it has been felt that if we knew what were the most popular plans for using money in bonds, these plans could be dramatized and stressed in advertising copy. For this reason people were asked in each drive what plans they had for their war bonds. Each time, over half of the people reported that they did not have any special plans for the use of their bonds. Among those who did have plans, however, the following were consistently the most popular:

1. To buy home or farm
2. To use for children's education
3. To keep as an emergency fund
4. To keep as a reserve for old age
5. To buy farm equipment or to make improvements

Plans for the use of war bonds to purchase gadgets, or even durable consumer goods such as automobiles or washing machines, were extremely infrequent.

Obstacles to Selling Bonds. Our attempt to get at the reasons people did not buy bonds in drives followed two main lines of approach. One was to ask people directly why they did not buy extra bonds, and the other was to ask a more projective question, namely, why do they think other people were not buying more bonds? Analysis of both approaches was quite useful.

Following the first approach, certain main conclusions were reached. First, the number of people who did not buy bonds because they had not heard of the campaign decreased strikingly as publicity became more effective. Second, in the early drives it was found that the main reason people gave for not buying bonds was that they could not afford to buy. As a result of this finding, a good deal of publicity was devoted in subsequent drives to the theme "You can't afford not to buy bonds." Third, a fairly large number of people, interviewed after the first public drive, said they had not bought because they were doing their share already. As stated earlier, this resulted from a misunderstanding of the purpose of the drive. Consequently, in the next drive the stress was put upon the purchase of an *extra* bond and the fact that a person was not doing his share unless he did buy extra bonds.

The second approach revealed two major motivational obstacles, namely, a fear that bonds might not be redeemed and a feeling that bonds were not sufficiently liquid. In regard to the first obstacle, little was accomplished in overcoming it. Efforts on the second one, though, met with some success. On the basis of our findings, along with other considerations, the Treasury decided in October 1944 to make bonds more readily redeemable through banks. As a result of this policy there was a striking decrease in complaints about the difficulty of cashing bonds.

Broader Background of Motivation. In deciding what appeals to use in future publicity, we have felt that it is important not only to know what motives were currently held by people, but also to understand something about the broader background out of which these reasons for buying emerged. Accordingly a fairly large portion of our research on motivation was devoted to this end.

The popular view of war financing was conceived in entirely personal terms. People somehow thought of Uncle Sam as taking money from the sale of bonds and putting it into his pocket, then taking it out of his pocket and buying planes and tanks with it. It was widely felt that if he did not get the money it would be impossible for him to buy weapons of war.

Following the Fourth War Loan Drive we asked people directly whether they believed that if enough bonds were not sold the boys would get enough supplies. The results were as follows: 46 per cent said that the boys would get the equipment even if bonds were not sold, 44 per cent said the boys would not get the equipment, the remaining 10 per cent said they did not know. The prevalence of this naïve view of war finance imposed restrictions upon the type of appeal which could most effectively be presented; but it also made it possible for those writing copy to sell war bonds without doing the more difficult job of basic education on war finance.

Closely related to this problem, of course, was the one of utilizing anti-inflation appeals in the sale of war bonds. We found repeatedly that people were quite deeply concerned about high prices. In the Fourth War Loan study, for example, 54 per cent of the people mentioned high prices as making it harder for them to get along financially, and 60 per cent said that they thought prices would probably rise as the war continued. These facts seemed to indicate that there was a potential motivation for bond buying which might be tapped if people could be convinced that bond buying would help keep prices down.

Even though so many people were concerned about high prices, when asked to give reasons for buying bonds only 19 per cent mentioned buying to prevent inflation. This figure remained highly stable throughout all of the drives.

The central core of the problem proved to be one of making people see just how the purchase of bonds could help to keep prices down. When asked directly whether or not they believed that bond buying would help keep prices down, 52 per cent of the people said "no," while 43 per cent gave an unqualified "yes," and an additional 3 per cent held that bonds were partially effective in keeping prices down. The basic educational job was never accomplished.

The third major area of research dealt with techniques for implementing sales.

Although we started out in the early drives conceiving of implementation in its broader meaning of all the facilities for selling bonds and direct face-to-face stimulation of sales, the emphasis in our research more and more concentrated on the question of solicitation. After the very earliest phases of the war bond program, we came to the general conclusion that there were sufficient outlets for the sale of bonds. For this reason research on implementation dealt largely with specific problems of solicitation.

Probably the most important finding from the First War Loan study was the following:

Four times as many of those who were solicited as those who were not bought extra bonds during April. Part of this difference is due to the fact that the solicitors went to the better prospects. But even allowing for this fact, it is clear that most people bought bonds *because they were asked to buy*.

Since solicitation was found to be so important in selling bonds, further analysis was made in various studies to find out what types of solicitors and what types of solicitation behavior were more effective.

In conjunction with the Fourth War Loan Drive, we made a special study of solicitors in a major city. By comparing groups of solicitors who had accomplished high sales with those who accomplished low or medium sales, certain conclusions could be drawn about the factors producing successful solicitation. In general, the main findings were that local urban communities which had high sales were organized earlier, had more active solicitors, and better neighborhood coverage than groups within the communities with low sales. The superior groups had arranged well in advance of the drives the following aspects of the campaign: organization of office details, recruiting of solicitors and assistant chairmen, training of solicitors, assignment of specific territory responsibility, establishment of methods for keeping sales records, and use of neighborhood appeals. In the superior groups the solicitors had careful training on drive mechanics, information on the necessity for high bond sales, discussions on effective sales approaches, special rallies to heighten enthusiasm, and an appreciation of the role of bonds in the war.

The ultimate test of all the techniques and methods used in selling bonds is to be found in the results. For this reason, measures of the participation of people in war bond campaigns constituted our fourth major area of study. A further consideration was also important. Although it would have been possible to raise the money for War Finance without selling bonds to large numbers of people, fiscal policy of the Treasury required that bonds be sold to as many people as possible. For this reason, figures on the number of people buying bonds were of great importance.

In the first public drive, 20 per cent of the income earners or their dependents purchased extra bonds. Buying reached an all-time high in the Fifth Drive when 47 per cent bought extra bonds. It should be noted that these figures refer to the purchase of extra bonds and do not refer to the total number of people buying bonds through payroll deduction or otherwise during the period of the drive.

An analysis of the number of people buying extra bonds in the various markets helped clarify needs for improving organization. In a typical survey the following facts were found: 50 per cent of the wage earners in the payroll market made extra purchases, compared to 41 per cent in the community market and 37 per cent in the farm market. Comparison of these figures with those measuring the number of people who bought regularly between drives showed that 83 per cent in the payroll market bought regularly between drives, 41 per cent in the community market, and only 11 per cent in the farm market. In other words, the markets which had the highest participation between drives were the ones that had the highest participation in drives. This fact resulted from the degree of permanent organization in the different markets so that solicitation was always highest in the payroll market, medium in the community market, and lowest among farmers.

These, then, are the major findings of one part of the research conducted for the War Finance Program. Many other problem areas associated with war finance were investigated by means of similar techniques. The brief summary presented here, however, should give some indication of the potentialities of a research program which combines into one coherent analysis data on attitudes, motives, information, and behavior. Only by getting all four types of data for the same individuals can full understanding of behavior be obtained or safe predictions of future behavior be projected.

INDEX

Acceptability, 141; criteria of, 147-48
ACKOFF, R. L., 1-7
ADAMIC, L., 63, 73
ADAMS, J. S. Jr., 6
Adaptability, 151
Advertising, 35, 89-90
Aesthetics, 51
Affective value, 41f
American Civilization, 9
American Society for Testing Materials, 123, 124, 134
American Standards Association, 134
Analysis of data, 18-19, 201-2
Analysis of variance, 163
ANSELM, ST., 99
Area sampling, 22-25, 28
ARISTOTLE, 51
ARMITT, F. M., 56n, 58
ASHCROFT, A. G., 133-34, 138, 142, 146, 147, 149
Attitudes, 17-18, 23-24, 50, 60f, 123, 199; employee, 177-98

BARTON, A. N., 155-63, 167, 174-75
Behavior patterns, 125
BENSON, E., 28, 29
BERGEN, H. B., 180, 190n
BERKELEY, 100
BEUTEL, F., 35, 36
Bias, 106f, 157; types, 115; of selection, 115-16; of samples, 167-70
BLANKENSHIP, A. B., 4, 16-19, 32, 38
BOK, E., 35
BOWLES, C., 88
BRAHE, TYCHO, 98
BREYER, R. F., 142-46
Bureau of Economic Research, 34
Bureau of Labor Statistics, 164
Bureau of the Budget, 169
Buyers, institutional, 149-52

Call-backs, 22-25, 28, 29, 33, 120
CARTWRIGHT, D., 198-209
Categories, 61f
CAYTON, H. R., 77

Census, 32, 34, 35, 113, 163-65, 172; Bureau, 32, 164-65; agriculture, 113; business, 113
Checks, 35-37
CHURCHMAN, C. W., 1-7, 122-32, 133-34
Clients, research, 16-19, 25-27
Coding, 201-2
Coefficient of variation, 114
Comparisons, 52; in stimulus, 43; paired, 43-44
Complete count, 5, 37, 113
Confidence intervals, 166
Confusion tests, 12-13
Consumer, education, 20-22, 86, 88; movement, 85f; Federation, 86-87; legislation, 87; strike, 89; definition of, 126; research, 136, 146; understanding by, 143; confidence, 144; guidance, 144; decision, 145; records, 157; purchase study (1936), 164
Consumers' Union, 85
Coöperation, 2, 6, 92-105, 133, 137, 138, 140, 152
Cornell technique, 60-84
Cost of sampling, 116, 120-22, 168-69, 176
COWAN, T. A., 6
Credit, 146
Criterion, psychological, 14; in surveys, 106-22; of data, 108-9; of acceptability, 147-49
Critical Idealism, 94f
CROSSLEY, A., 11-13, 24, 37
Cross-scale analysis, 38
Cross section, 163, 166
CURTISS, J. H., 146-49
Cutting points, 70

DRAKE, S. C., 77
DEDRICK, C. L., 121n
Definitions, 124-25; operational, 138
DEMING, W. E., 6, 34-37, 106-22, 128, 167-70, 200
Department of Agriculture, 198; Graduate School of, 117n
Department of Commerce, 25
DESCARTES, 95-97, 99-100